Composer to composer

Composer to composer
Conversations *about* contemporary music

Andrew Ford

Photographs by
Malcolm Crowthers & Belinda Webster

QUARTET BOOKS

to my parents,
Marjorie and Alec Ford

Photographs ©:
  Malcolm Crowthers Photography
  40 Buckingham Palace Rd, Victoria, London SWI
  Tel: 071–1828–4894 Fax: 071–233–8971

  Belinda Webster
  PO Box 373, Glebe NSW 2037 Australia

First published in Great Britain by Quartet Books Limited 1993
A member of the Namara Group
27/29 Goodge Street
London W1P 1FD

This edition published by arrangement with Allen & Unwin Pty Ltd,
Australia

A catalogue record for this title is available from the British Library

ISBN 0 7043 7061 1

Set in 10/11 pt Goudy by DOCUPRO, Sydney
Printed by Chong Moh Offset Printing, Singapore

Contents

Preface

Whilst I have always been fascinated to read interviews with creative people, this book came about almost by accident. In 1988, at the request of Belinda Webster, I interviewed Pierre Boulez for the Sydney radio station 2MBS-FM. People seemed to like it: a part of the interview appeared in the *Sydney Morning Herald*; another part was broadcast on *Arts National*, ABC radio's weekly arts magazine program. Over the next few years I interviewed other composers, until it finally struck me that I had the makings of a book.

Partly because of its piecemeal origins and partly because of the different media for which the interviews were done, the present volume has a varied format. Certain interviews took place under PR conditions: a maximum of half an hour, with a queue of journalists waiting their turns outside the door; others were far more leisurely. Some had to be written up quickly as news stories; with others there was time to construct a more considered piece. Some of the interviews in this book are appearing in print for the first time. Of those which have been published elsewhere, none is unchanged, although I have attempted to preserve the style of the original piece (whether it was written for a newspaper or an arts magazine).

All of the composers included are people I find personally interesting, even if I would not necessarily want to write their music. Naturally, it would have been perfectly possible to assemble a list of 30 other composers, perhaps equally interesting and equally articulate. A few well-known composers have not made it into the book because our paths failed to cross; some with whom I sought meetings preferred not to be interviewed; others merely slipped through my net. The composers included are largely English-speaking. This is because I have spent most of my time over the last few years in Australia, with visits to the United States and Britain. I regret the fact that there are no Asian-based composers in the book: a planned visit to Japan failed to eventuate.

Any well-informed reader of this volume will doubtless have his or her own list of preferred interviewees. Likewise, in some places readers will wish that a certain question had been asked, a particular line of

viii *Composer to composer*

thought pursued. It could hardly be otherwise. But I hope that you will feel that the composers I have spoken to have allowed themselves to be captured, if only for a moment or two. Because that, it seems to me, is what an interview is: a record of a particular person's thoughts on a particular day.

The preparation of a book like this requires the co-operation and assistance of many people. First, thanks must go to the composers who responded with patience and even enthusiasm to my questions about their work; also to Peter Grimshaw of Boosey & Hawkes (Sydney) and Richard Paine of Music Sales (Sydney), and to others at publishing houses in New York and London, whose efforts made it possible to set up many of the meetings.

Many of these interviews originally appeared in slightly different forms in *24 Hours*, the *Sydney Morning Herald* and *Australian Society*, or on radio stations ABC-FM, Radio National and 2MBS-FM. I am grateful to them all for allowing me to reprint them here.

The University of Wollongong was most generous with funding for this project, and my colleagues in the School of Creative Arts were supportive, good-humoured and remarkably flexible when it came to my occasional absences from campus in pursuit of yet another composer. I would also like to thank my students for their interest and enthusiasm for this project, and for their questions and suggestions which, they may be surprised to learn, have been of very great assistance to me.

I must thank several individual people who assisted and encouraged me in my endeavours. Belinda Webster is in many ways responsible for this book, since it was she who first asked me to interview a composer. To Rhonda Black, Lynne Frolich and Julia Hancock of Allen & Unwin, and to my editor Gillian Gillett I am grateful for encouragement and many useful suggestions. Other editors and producers have been by turns generous, instructive and inspiring with their advice; they include Penny Lomax, Maureen Cooney, Wendy McLeod, Peter Cochrane, Angela Benny, Peter Browne and especially the editor of *24 Hours*, Suzy Baldwin.

To friends who tolerated my occasionally obsessive behaviour whilst putting this book together, and who offered much useful advice, I am indebted. In particular I wish to thank the following, who patiently listened to me think aloud about what I was trying to do here, and who helped me clarify my intentions: Martin Buzacott, Nick Chapman, Graham Devlin, Marcia Doheny, Cesca Eaton, Gerald English, Mary Finsterer, Kathleen Gallagher, Helen Gilbart, Bronwen Jones, Tim Pye and Cathy Strickland. Finally, I wish to thank Margaret Morgan for her great support, as well as for her endless editorial wisdom.

Andrew Ford
Sydney 1993

Introduction

In David Lynch's movie *The Elephant Man* there is a memorable scene in which John Hurt, standing on a railway platform with a sack on his head, bellows the line 'I am not an animal'. I hope my media friends will not take it too personally, then, when I assert, with all the strength I can muster, that I am not a journalist.

When I interview a composer, I am not interested in writing an exposé, or ferreting out some deep dark secret (unless of course they have one they particularly want to confess). I want to let them speak about their work and their attitudes to their work. I feel that interviewing is rather like painting a portrait. I try to allow the composer's real personality to emerge, although I am even more interested in musical personality, and these are not always the same thing. When interviews have appeared in print, I have experienced what I take to be the anxiety of the portrait painter: will the subject approve; will the sitter even recognise him or herself? Responses have normally been gratifying, although, for the record, Nigel Butterley thought he came across a touch humourless (which, I can confirm, he isn't).

Once, on live radio, an interviewer asked me what sort of music I composed. This is the question all composers dread, because in order to answer it one needs to know how much knowledge the questioner has, and it's rude to ask. Playing for time, I think I probably said, 'What do you mean?'

'Well is it like Beethoven or Bach?' the interviewer persisted.

'No,' I said.

'So what *is* it like?'

'It's like me,' I replied, lamely, but truthfully enough.

I think I have an advantage, then, when I go to speak to a composer, in that I write music too. If I have never met the composer before, I will not always let on about this, but I will let on very quickly that I know the composer's music well. The relief on the part of the interviewee is often palpable, and (to employ a real journalist's phrase) my foot is in the door.

I would hardly say that I have an interview technique, but it might be worth briefly describing my approach to these conversations. As I have suggested, I try to know the composer's music as well as possible: composers are always more talkative when you can mention specific pieces and ask specific questions about them—it is as though they feel they are speaking to someone who cares about their work (which was always true, whether I actually liked it or not).

I think about the questions I will ask, but, unless I feel particularly intimidated, will not write them down. Quite apart from producing a certain stilted quality in the conversation, prepared questions tend to impose a structure on the interview and make one less attentive to the composer's answers and less inclined to ask follow-up questions. When I go to an interview with a list of questions, I generally do not refer to it. It is simply my safety net.

I try to keep the conversation on musical matters, although certain composers (Sir Michael Tippett, for instance) would rather talk about almost any other subject, whereas some are rendered semi-articulate when asked to describe in words working methods which are, by definition, non-verbal (Birtwistle would be a good example of this). Some composers would rather be anywhere else than in front of a microphone (Meale); others come across as professional interviewees (Boulez: notice that, as a 'professional interviewee' he has the knack of *not* answering certain questions—for instance, the one about which sort of piece earns the Boulez imprimatur). Some composers give interviews because it would be impolite to refuse (I suspect Cage was like that); others talk to you as though they wish to set the record straight (Reich). It is important to remember that everyone in this book (including myself) works, first and foremost, in sound rather than words. The reader will have to imagine the occasional groping for a phrase or the teasing-out of a meaning that have occurred in many of these interviews.

Only six of the 30 composers in this book are women. Some readers may be shocked at this imbalance; others will, perhaps, be surprised that there are so many. In Australia today roughly fifteen per cent of composers are female, so the ratio seems about right. I felt obliged to allow these six composers the opportunity to discuss their position as part of a minority group (aware that I was not asking their male colleagues to pontificate on how their gender affected their work). Saariaho and Weir spoke a little reluctantly on the subject, Henderson raised the topic herself, Gubaidulina had been too busy fighting political oppression of another kind to have had time to think much about it.

The setting for the interview is often out of my hands: one is told where to go and when. If I do have a say in the matter, I prefer to go to the composer's home, or to do the interview in a bar or restaurant. The greater informality of the latter is well worth the inevitable extraneous noise when I transcribe the tape.

The final format of the interview—whether it be written up or straight Q&A—is dictated by the nature of the conversation. I am not only interested in whether it flows well, but also in whether the composer's personality comes across from a straight transcription. Most often it doesn't. This is not necessarily because the composer is inarticulate, indeed it is frequently the reverse: orally articulate people often employ a great many shades of tone of voice which vanish in transcription; without these, the written word can have little intensity or even meaning.

When I began to think of these interviews in terms of a book, there was no subject as such. A number of friends asked me what the book was about and I was able only to respond that it was about composers. But in assembling these pieces I now see that there is a good deal of overlap in the areas covered, and that this does give the volume as a whole a certain thrust.

One of the most frequently invoked names is that of Anton Webern (1883-1945). Webern's music is seldom performed these days and, with many composers (as with audiences), is rather unpopular. And yet it seems that he is indeed a touchstone of sorts for late-20th century composers, whether they regard his music as an important example or simply as anathema. Another reference point is the festival of new music at Darmstadt in Germany. It was at this festival, in the years following the second world war, that many of the ideas which came to characterise post-Webernian music first took root.

Finally, what John Cage described as the 'multiplicity' of styles in late 20th century music might be considered this book's principal theme, and, in particular, how composers respond to working in an environment in which 'What sort of music do you compose?' is such a pertinent question to ask, and nearly impossible to answer.

Elliott Carter

Gentility and apocalypse

Elliott Carter

'I do think people are worried about the modern world', said Elliott
Carter. 'I think there's a very strong fear of the present and of the
future, and I must say I even sometimes have it myself. There's one
view of the future that we're heading for disaster, but that started back
before Chaucer. In fact I think it's in the Bible.'

From Elliott and Helen Carter's Greenwich Village apartment there
is a fine view of the World Trade Center. The angle is such that a mere
crack of sky separates the Center's twin towers. 'On a windy day,' Mrs
Carter informed me, 'that crack closes.'

Such an apocalyptic image, such a confrontation between nature
and the 20th century, seems an entirely appropriate thing for Elliott
Carter to witness from his window. Carter's music is concerned with
living in the modern world (and where better to be than the heart of
New York City to keep in touch with that?). But it is also frequently
about nature—particularly the elements, and especially wind. His Concerto for Orchestra (1969), based upon St John Perse's poem 'Winds',
and A *Symphony of Three Orchestras* (1976), inspired by Hart Crane's
'The Bridge', both leave the listener feeling weather-beaten. I discovered recently that a flute piece which was on Carter's work desk when
I visited him has since been given the title *Scrivo in vento* (Written on
the Wind).

I had been told that visiting the Carters was like going to see one's
grandparents. Their hospitality is well known: I took them gifts, but
left with more. Still, Carter's reputation as a figure of importance in
20th century music is such that I was nervous making my way through
the stifling mid-summer streets of the Village. Few places on earth are
more oppressive than Manhattan on a hot, humid day. Carter is arguably
the most respected composer in the world today—respected, in particular, by other composers. *This* other composer, sweltering in the heat,
was conscious of large wet stains on his linen jacket and shoes that
were starting to squelch as he walked.

I arrived at the apartment a cross between a beetroot and a water sprinkler, to be greeted with an 'Oh my' from Mr Carter, a glass of iced tea and a seat next to the airconditioner.

Elliott Carter did not seem tired, as his publisher had warned me he would. He listened most attentively to questions he must have heard a hundred times before, answering them thoughtfully and often at length. I asked him about his early life, and especially the formative artistic milieu in which he grew up.

'From my earliest days,' Carter said, '—really since I was 15 or 16—I have been interested in the modernist movement. All the interest in music came entirely from hearing Stravinsky and Varèse. I did not start as most musicians did during those years—and even now—with old music.

'I have always been interested in contemporary painting. I have the works of Proust from when they first came out; I read the works of James Joyce as they first came out; I've been going through my books and I have first editions of most of the works of that period. So my point of view has always been connected with what is called modernism, and I stick with it. Sometimes it goes out of fashion, but it comes back again.'

Just at the moment modernism seems to be going through one of its unfashionable periods, and yet Carter's music retains its admirers, even amongst those composers whose own styles are quite radically different. But if Carter 'sticks with' modernism, how precisely would he describe its characteristics and what attracted him to them?

'In music the concern with an expanded vocabulary which Stravinsky, Varèse and Schoenberg introduced before the first world war—and after—is what I considered modernism to be. Not only the whole field of dissonance, but also new points of view about rhythm and new sonorities: that was one aspect of it. Another one was that we were living in a world that had been completely changed by the writings of Freud, and the whole sense of the subconscious and the conscious were much more intricately involved than we had thought.

'Certainly one of the aspects of modernism that interested me as a young person was that it made people angry. I remember, for instance, when Dimitri Mitropoulos played my old *Holiday* overture here and we went out in Carnegie Hall to take a bow together, he pointed to the audience and said, "Those are our enemies". That was something that, as a young person, impressed me.'

The *Holiday* overture, composed in 1944, is typical of the music Carter was writing at that period. It is a celebration of the liberation of Paris, where the composer had studied with Nadia Boulanger ten years earlier, and—far from seeming provocative—its mood is broadly popularist in that overtly 'American' manner of Carter's slightly older contemporary Aaron Copland. I asked the composer how he now felt about these works, whose style he had moved far away from only five years later.

'Well, I'm a rather arrogant man. I look back on those pieces and think that, for what they are, they're rather good. I see no reason to write like that now, but at the time that I wrote them I believed that's what I should do. I believed that a composer had a responsibility toward his society and should write something that was, so to speak, acceptable to the society that had nurtured him. However, it began to be obvious to me that this is a very noble thought, but it doesn't hold water really because society is such an amorphous and uncertain thing that you really can't know this. And it might be that you're really serving the society better writing something that is striking and original and unusual, than by writing something that is immediately accessible to the public.

'There are some cases in the past—even in the 20th century—where composers wrote things which were unacceptable to the general public which finally became useful and helpful to them. When I was young, for instance, the Mahler symphonies were very rarely played and people didn't like them very much: they thought they were rather vulgar and excessive. But this whole attitude toward Mahler has changed enormously. When I was a student in Boston, they used to say the exit sign meant "This way in case of Brahms". So this is a long story; it's not something simple. If Brahms and Mahler had written music—as some of their contemporaries did—which was immediately accessible, they might have been forgotten.'

Elliott Carter's early creativity, fuelled by his experiences of modern music at concerts in Greenwich Village, was greatly encouraged by his friendship with the composer Charles Ives. But Carter's family was not especially enthusiastic about a musical career, and he was packed off to Harvard where he studied English, philosophy, mathematics and classics. The conservativeness of Harvard's musical establishment meant that Carter was more than happy not to be studying music there, although, before heading for Paris, he returned to the university to enrol in a Masters degree, working with Walter Piston and Gustav Holst.

Paradoxically, of all Carter's studies it is probably his undergraduate work which has had most relevance to his mature music. Even in his non-vocal pieces, there is frequently some literary or philosophical impulse behind the notes, and Carter believes that music can (and by and large should) be as complex as the best philosophy or poetry.

In 1950 Carter's growing disillusion with the music he was writing led him to take a sort of sabbatical in the Sonora desert in Arizona. There he began to compose his first string quartet, a big piece of a technical difficulty which still makes great demands upon players, but, at the time, must have seemed virtually unapproachable. Significantly, the quartet was written without a commission and 'largely for my own satisfaction'. It proved to be a turning-point both in Carter's music and his career, winning for him the first prize in the Concours à quatuor at Liège in Belgium and, at its subsequent performance, firmly establishing Carter's European reputation. To this day, Carter's music is more frequently performed and highly regarded in Europe than in the United States. In 1988, for example, the city of Turin mounted a celebration of the composer's 80th birthday which aimed to include performances of every one of Carter's pieces. The American celebrations that year were considerably more modest.

Carter's music since that first quartet has been some of the most original composed in the post-war period. He has followed his own path, never writing serial music, even when the musical establishment considered it de rigueur, and having even less interest in the chance operations of his Greenwich Village neighbour John Cage. He eschewed not only the advancing technology of tape recorders, live electronics and computers, which bedazzled many of his colleagues, but special effects per se: in Carter's scores there is very little use of extended playing techniques. There is a kind of purity about Carter's music which stems from its reliance upon the traditional elements of pitch and rhythm as its principal organising features.

For Carter, each musical work is a new departure. Just as he consciously tried something different with the first quartet, he immediately moved on to find new challenges.

'I never wrote a work like [the first string quartet] again, because I felt that I had done that and then I wanted to go on to something else. I've tried to make each of my pieces individual and separate from each other; I didn't want to repeat myself. I hope each of my pieces has a distinct character of its own—a distinct style of its own, almost. When I came to write a piece like my Violin Concerto [1990] and started dividing it up into movements, people said I was becoming very conservative. While that may be true, that wasn't what I was thinking about: I was thinking that I never wrote a piece using the structure of three different movements before.'

There certainly are, however, compositional methods which Carter has employed on a number of occasions. One of these is the large-scale rhythmic organisation of his music, related to what the composer has described as the 'time screen'. This is a metaphor for the way in which music is 'projected' in or against time, and it has led its composer to construct for many of his works a fundamental pulse, too slow to be perceived by his listeners, which acts as a rhythmic skeleton on which the music is then fleshed out. Carter provides a more down-to-earth analogy for this.

'In *Night Fantasies* [for solo piano; 1980] there's a rhythmic plan, and all of the music is hung on it like clothes in a closet. The plan runs from the beginning to the end of the piece. This is not something which is new. In the music of the past there were these four-bar and eight-bar phrases that went on mercilessly for enormous lengths of time. When Mendelssohn or someone else breaks that, it is very obvious that he intended to break it. In other words there was a plan there, and then there is a distortion of the plan—which I also do, of course.

'Most of my pieces of the last five or six years have a big rhythmic plan that is very loose—there are big, slow beats which run through the whole piece. Now then, what I come up with in detail is very free and very different.

'I am rather impatient with easy solutions, so that sometimes I can't think how to begin a piece for days, although I have a very good idea of what happens in the middle. But I worry about it until finally something shows up. Very often I write little examples of what I would like to hear in the piece and then I assemble them in one way or another. *Night Fantasies* was written in that way. I wrote lots of little fragments and then gradually adapted them to the big rhythmic scheme.'

It is a method which Stravinsky is often said to have used: writing small blocks of musical material, and then moving them around until they fit. One report speaks of Stravinsky's use of a scrapbook for this purpose. Certainly the new flute piece on Elliott Carter's desk appeared to be a scissor-and-paste job.

'I'm very concerned with causality', Carter explains further, 'that whatever happens in a piece has to seem to have a reason for happening. In this little flute piece I had the idea that I'd like to have the flute play a series of things in which one bit was in the very lowest register and then the next bit was in the very highest. And after writing a piece which did that, I decided I didn't know how to begin it. Because you have the flute playing something very slow and quiet in the low register and then you have some very high notes, and it was important to suggest what is the reason that this suddenly happens this way. And so today I wrote a whole beginning which explained all that.'

This impression of an artisan's approach to building a piece of music, however, is at odds with the nature of the finished product. Carter's music is, above all, highly expressive. It is also surprisingly non-abstract. Each piece is, in a sense, a drama in which different instruments are allocated individual characteristics, and their interrelations generate the musical content of the piece. This would not be so very remarkable were it not for the fact that Carter views his instrumental characters anthropomorphically. His pieces are almost models of society.

'I never think of my pieces in the abstract. Very early in the piece the general typecasting of the various instruments or groups of instruments becomes something that is, to me, a means of expression of a certain specific idea, like a human idea: the idea of groups of people in society; individuals and their relationships to each other. My music has been very concerned with the presentation of individual characters and their interrelation. Certainly the second, third and fourth string quartets all deal with this particular combination of various characters. In the second and fourth quartets I've isolated the four players as having different sorts of characters, and I've kept pretty much to that from beginning to end. In the third quartet they are two pairs: the individuals in one pair are quite similar to each other, but the two pairs are quite different.

'In almost all my recent works there has been this element of dichotomy of character and the interplay between them. This actually comes from opera. The thought itself came from reading Edward Dent's book on Mozart's operas, which describes this in detail. And then there's a moment in one of the essays of Schoenberg about how Mozart was able to combine, in one ensemble, three or four different kinds of characters, and sometimes put them together in counterpoint, and sometimes separate them in a sequence. My music has been very concerned about that.'

In an attempt to make these dramas clear in his music, Carter has frequently allocated not only specific harmonic tendencies to his instrumental characters, but also individual gestures, rhythmic types, playing techniques and general 'character notes'. In the second quartet, for example, the first violin is a show-off ('fantastic, ornate, mercurial'), whereas the second violin 'has a laconic, orderly character which is sometimes humorous'. In an attempt to bring still greater clarity to these multi-voiced works, Carter has sometimes resorted to the spacial separation of his performers. In the third quartet (1971), the two duos of violin and viola, and violin and cello are as far apart from each other on stage as possible. For all this, the complexity of Carter's musical ideas and the high technical demands his works make on their players have landed the composer and his work with a reputation for impenetrability.

'I try to make my music as clear as I can. What's rewarding is that in the end, when I supervise the performances, and the players do it as I imagine it, it doesn't sound that complicated. What produces the sense of confusion very often is that the players themselves don't know what the various levels of sound are: they are not able to keep the dominating thing clearly dominating the things that are secondary, and the background in the background. I've heard performances of Richard Strauss that were very confusing for the same reason: the work gives a sense of greater complexity than it really has.

'But the word "complexity" is a very misleading one in itself. The perception of a human being can reduce complex things to simple things. We are surrounded on every side of our lives by things that, as soon as you start looking at them closely, seem to be extremely complex. A piece of wood is a very complex object, and yet is a very simple one. And I like to think of my music that, on one level, it is perfectly simple what is happening; on another level, the texture is rather varied and is constantly changing. It varies between dense things and transparent things; between one line and then 20 lines. It is constantly progressing from one idea to another, so that all this seems like a complicated thing, I suppose, to some people.'

The great rhythmic flexibility which characterises these shifts in Carter's music is one of its most remarkable features. It is as though, in Oliver Knussen's happy phrase, the music were 'hitched up to a multi-speed gearbox'. But this very flexibility itself can create problems of performance (and, consequently, of audience perception), especially in the orchestral works. After a quintet for piano and winds ('like the Mozart quintet'), which Carter is writing for an ensemble including the pianist András Schiff and the oboist Heinz Holliger, there are two new orchestral commissions ahead, for the New York Philharmonic and the BBC Symphony. Much of the composer's most powerful music of the last 25 years has been orchestral, but Carter is increasingly doubtful about the point of composing for this institution.

'I feel that the orchestra is a lost cause: it's too expensive and too much trouble. If you write very original music, nowadays the orchestras in America haven't time to rehearse it. They try sometimes, and with a good deal of good will they can raise the thousands of dollars it takes to have the extra rehearsals. And then the public doesn't see why they should have bothered to do it when they hear the music. The two big pieces I've written—the Concerto for Orchestra and *A Symphony of Three Orchestras*—have seldom been performed in America and in almost every case not well, except for the performances of Leonard Bernstein and Pierre Boulez. But in Europe these works get played comparatively frequently. It seems like a waste of my effort to write something that'll get played very rarely and mostly not well.

'The Violin Concerto has had ten or more performances in Europe and two here. That's very discouraging to me: to live in this country and have few performances of my orchestral music. I think that orchestras are on the way out: their public hasn't developed. It's the same with the opera, I think. And composers who do get played always write things that are very conservative, so that it doesn't take too much rehearsal and the audiences will like it fairly quickly.'

Carter identifies this problem with audiences as something deep-seated.

'It's very different today from the end of the 19th century. Then, the people in society who had money were often more cultivated than they are now, and it makes a difference. We're always being condemned as being elitist in our field, but the entire repertory of classical music was written for an elite. The Beethoven symphonies were not written for the general public of Vienna.

'Composers today have got this standard of older music which encourages us to write skilfully and sensitively and full of awareness of the musical past and its wonders. And we have a different kind of audience than that music was written for. It's a very puzzling paradox. I don't think about it much.'

And, with that, Mrs Carter enters the room to ask if I have a wife. She hands me a gift-wrapped box which I am to take home for her as a memento of New York. It contains a silk scarf and a pair of earrings. It is at this point that I am shown the view of the World Trade Center and told of its worrying habit of bending with the wind. And there seems to be a useful image here in this confluence of gentility and apocalypse.

Elliott Carter is a man whose point of view is, to use his description of 19th century concert-goers, 'cultivated'. He reputedly heads off bouts of insomnia by conjugating irregular German, Italian and Greek verbs. Sadly, it must be admitted that such erudition is rare today, and that the Carters belong to a bygone era. And yet, every time he sits down with his manuscript paper, scissors and paste, Elliott Carter unleashes a music both complex in its intellectual rigour and elemental in its often violent expressivity.

One vivid image I have of Carter and his music is that of the audience at a 1975 performance of his Concerto for Orchestra with Boulez conducting the New York Philharmonic. The piece is one of its composer's most powerful, complex and violent creations. It lifts you up and transports you at terrifying speed, as through a musical vortex, before simply stopping, leaving you still hurtling through space. The whole experience is both emotional and provocative.

The audience at that concert was visibly shaken, but what I recall so clearly is the expression on their faces as the diminutive, smiling, avuncular figure of the composer made his way onto the platform to share in the applause. It was like that moment in *The Wizard of Oz*, when the dog Toto tugs at the curtain beside the Wizard's mask, to reveal a little old man working the controls. The difference is that, far from being a fraud, Elliott Carter is arguably one of the most genuinely important artists of the late 20th century.

New York City, June 1991

Ellen Taaffe Zwilich

A very magical thing

Ellen Taaffe Zwilich

When I first met Ellen Taaffe Zwilich, in 1988, she had just attended the American premiere of her orchestral piece *Symbolon* by the New York Philharmonic under Zubin Mehta. The performance was given at the Lincoln Center in mid-town Manhattan, as the opening work of the first New York International Festival of the Arts. It was only the American premiere, because the work had previously been performed in Leningrad and Moscow during the orchestra's historic *glasnost* tour. Such was the type of commission coming the way of the first woman to win a Pulitzer Prize for composition.

We arranged to meet at the artists' entrance to Avery Fisher Hall and made our way through the grey concrete warren of staircases and corridors that is the backstage of every modern concert hall in the world. Finally we arrived at a tiny dressing room, and I set up my tape recorder on the low table between us. What I remember most about our conversation that morning was Ms Zwilich's good humour: for half an hour we laughed uproariously.

Four years later I am in an ABC studio in Sydney; Ellen Zwilich is in an ABC studio in New York. There are thousands of kilometres and a satellite between us. What impresses me most this time—almost to the point of scepticism—is that she so clearly remembers our previous meeting. It is she who reminds me about that little cupboard of a dressing room. I am briefly sceptical only because between 1988 and 1992, Ellen Zwilich has been very busy, fulfilling one commission after another—most of them orchestral. Unlike many of her colleagues, who have accepted attachments to the excellent Meet-the-Composer residency scheme run by American orchestras, Zwilich has had far too many commitments to consider the possibility. So, that she should remember a half-hour interview from four years ago—at a time when she was inundated with half-hour interviews—is, it seems to me, remarkable.

Ellen Taaffe (pronounced 'Tafe') was born and raised in Florida. Her initial training was as a pianist, trumpeter and violinist. The violin won out at university, and a professional career ensued in New York City.

'I think almost all of my life I have aspired to be a musician. That's taken different turns at different points in my life: writing music has always been very important to me, it's just that it moved ever more to the centre of my life. At this point I don't really have time to practise the violin, so I don't play the violin any more.

'I do believe that the history of music is the history of the inter-relationship of performance and composition. Many of the composers of the past were the major performers of the day. I think there's a dilemma for the modern composer, because to be a performer today means that—unless you play only your own music—you're required to play music across a very broad spectrum. I'm not sure that this is the right environment for a composer. I think you have to be very much in touch with your own feelings and your own ideas and your own aims and what music means to *you* at your very heart and soul. I have found it very rewarding to be able to spend a great deal of my time listening only to the music that I feel is important to listen to, or that I want to listen to—being involved only with music that is somehow related to what I'm doing.'

In saying, effectively, that a composer should be a specialist, Zwilich is echoing the sentiments of many other composers. Harrison Birtwistle, for example, has remarked that composers should go to extremes, 'so that no one can mistake your meaning'; Boulez once argued strongly in favour of intolerance as an important part of a young composer's make-up. Zwilich, however, insists that to be a composer today also requires considerable maturity and seriousness of mind.

'In the past, a composer was often a child prodigy and I think in the late 20th century—and we're really looking at the 21st century right now—that art is a very meaningful province for the grown-up: you bring a philosophy to it, you bring life experience, you bring a modern mind-set of making informed choices.'

But does this kind of attitude not leave Zwilich wide open to those charges which are inevitably levelled at a composer of concert music in the late 20th century—charges of élitism? Is she concerned that her music may appeal to only a small (educated? privileged?) sector of society?

'So many things in the modern world, whether they are Australian or North American, are to do with the mass market. I think it's a perfectly plausible thing for a person to do with their life—to find some small corner that is not necessarily something that reaches the widest possible audience, but may be very meaningful to a smaller audience. That doesn't bother me at all. I'm very concerned with the audience, and it's very gratifying to me that my music does reach people, that performers want to do it, and that it means something to them. But this may be far, far fewer people than, say, [those who] listen to Madonna or M.C. Hammer. This doesn't bother me.'

In 1964, still considering herself primarily a violinist, Ellen Taaffe Zwilich moved to New York City, where she played under Leopold

Stokowski in the American Symphony Orchestra. Concurrently, she enrolled in a doctoral program at the Juilliard School. Here her mentors were Roger Sessions and Elliott Carter.

'Roger Sessions was my principal teacher really. When I was with him I made my greatest strides. In fact I've had considerable difficulty in pinpointing exactly what it was that I got from Roger Sessions; all I know is that he kind of stood by me as I found my own voice as a composer, and I don't think there is a greater gift that a teacher can give you than that.'

Whatever it was that Zwilich got from Sessions and Carter, it was certainly not their musical styles. Listeners to Zwilich's music would be hard pressed to hear much obvious influence of either of her teachers.

'No, I don't hear anything either, and this to me seems perfectly normal. I think there's something basically a bit maverick about someone who wants to write music. I don't believe these people who say that they heard so-and-so's music and they wanted to write just like that composer. It seems to me the impulse is very different. I've never wanted to write just like somebody else, or to adopt a particular style; I think of composition as something much more profound than just your stylistic approach.'

There is, however, an apparent paradox about this, given the critical response to her most recent music. It is not that, like some of her colleagues, Zwilich has made a conscious decision to overthrow modernity or to embrace neo-romanticism; Ellen Zwilich's musical expression has simply been distilled to its essentials, and the catalyst for this seems to have been a personal crisis.

In the late 1960s Ellen Taaffe married Joseph Zwilich (pronounced 'Zwilish'), a fellow violinist in New York who played for the Metropolitan Opera. In 1979 he died suddenly. At the time, Ellen Zwilich was composing a chamber concerto, and this work became a musical memorial to her late husband. The piece marks a watershed in the composer's stylistic development: she seems to have stopped thinking about style at all. Six years later—in the *New York Times*—she summed it up in this way: 'Everything had changed. Suddenly all talk of method and style seemed trivial. I wanted to say something, musically, about life and living . . . We've had to come to grips with an incredible amount of evil and pain in this century . . . but this agony is only one reality; we shouldn't forget beauty, joy, nobility, and love—greater realities which artists must learn to express once again.'

So if, today, Ellen Taaffe Zwilich sometimes speaks in a manner which seems uncompromising, the critical response to her music has tended to employ words such as 'accessible' and 'pleasing'. This would suggest that she consciously takes her audience into account.

'I think, maybe a quarter of a century from now, people will look back and find it very difficult to understand what we were talking about in the 1990s when we spoke of music being accessible. I mean of course music ought to be able to reach people; this doesn't mean that it's going to reach every last person. I'm not at all insulted when people say my music is accessible—I think that means that I'm human like the listeners and the performers.'

But whom does Ellen Zwilich think of when she composes? Does she write to please herself or to please an audience? And, if the latter, which audience? There is a small pause as she considers her answer.

'I don't know whether this is a terrible admission or something, but I write because I have to; I write out of some need in myself.

'When I'm writing I do think about the performer. For instance, I've just finished my third symphony—for the New York Philharmonic—and in my head as I was working on this it was not just like an abstract B natural in such-and-such an octave or on such-and-such an instrument, but I was hearing this orchestra that has played so much of my music—I was hearing these people play it in my mind. That is a tremendous stimulus to me; it gets me flooded with ideas. And sometimes in my mind I have a picture of the New York Philharmonic sitting there waiting for my music to be put on their stands.

'I do feel that ultimately all of the arts are about human experience on a very profound level and that it's our shared experience that causes us to feel the communication. So if a composer is not just putting notes together, but allowing the wealth of our experience and our feelings and this kind of magical thing called music to come out of us and reach out to other people, then I think that is the . . . fulcrum, you might say, of the musical experience.'

Just as the influence of Sessions and Carter is seldom if ever audible in Zwilich's music, it is equally difficult to find much evidence of the composer's great interest in Arnold Schoenberg. It is true that the cogently argued structures of Zwilich's scores might be traced back to the leader of the second Viennese school, but in terms of her musical language, she is probably closest to Schoenberg's late works—pieces which are still damned as untenable and reactionary by many of his admirers. I asked which aspects of Schoenberg's work were of most importance to her.

'I think that Schoenberg was one of the most important thinkers about music in this century, and it's impossible to be a young composer—or at least a composer of my generation—without coming to terms with him in some way. I do think that there was a whole breath of fresh air that came out of the new Vienna school, to do with thinking about tonal relationships. I think that when people 25 or 30 years down the pike look back at this era, they'll find a lot more continuity than perhaps most people see at the moment. I think they'll see and even hear connections between things that we think of as unrelated.'

It is often said that the final years of the 20th century seem to be a period of stocktaking. Following the extraordinary musical developments of the first 25 years of this century, during which composers as different as Debussy and Schoenberg, Stravinsky and Berg, Bartók and Webern all pursued radical stylistic paths, there have been few revolutions in music. Now, at the end of the century, we are perhaps able to put those early years into perspective and see what was important—at least what was important for each of us personally. Is this what Zwilich means by finding those connections?

'Yes. Although I don't agree with "stocktaking". You see I think a composer is doing something out of a basic drive. And it's not to exemplify a style or even to mirror your own period. You can't *help* mirroring your own period: you live in your own time, you are of that time, and whatever you do will in some way be of that time. If we consider the history of music, we look at techniques, we look at the growth and development of certain ideas, but I don't think that's the basic impulse of the composer—at least it's not at all *my* impulse. I do think there's quite a natural continuity. For instance, today I think that most listeners find it hard to understand why there were riots over the first performance of *The Rite of Spring*: that music seems to us to grow so naturally out of the Russian music that Stravinsky grew up knowing and the French traditions that he was immersed in—it doesn't seem like a break at all. I think that what has grown out of the new ways of thinking of Schoenberg and others is a new concept of tonality in the broadest sense of the term, where you really do have a twelve-tone tonality which is *possibly* becoming a kind of common language. I don't know because I'm really interested in things much more basic than language. After all, language and ideas and feelings can be somewhat separate can't they?

'I find myself interested in an ever broader palette; a wider range of expression: that's what I'm focusing on. Of course one *works* with language and different pieces have a slightly different approach to language. I think my music is very connected, one piece to another, but certainly I'm always changing and in fact that's something that I very much enjoy about composing. I like the idea of being in a continuum, not only with my own past, but with the music of the past and the present; having these connections and yet always trying something a little new; you know, jumping into the water not quite sure of whether you can swim.

'I think music is a very magical thing. I mean we talk about it and try to tame it and codify it and put it into a nice little box and put a red ribbon on it. But it's much more mysterious and profound than that. When you think of the music that touches you, it's not all of one period or one composer or one kind of music. When a piece touches you and really changes your life—as happens to all of us who love music—something is happening that's really, to me, beyond reach of the verbal. Maybe, if I could say it in words, I wouldn't have to write music.'

New York–Sydney, April 1992

Pierre Boulez

Creating the spirit

Pierre Boulez

As part of the events to mark the bicentenary of the European settle-
ment of Australia, the Ensemble InterContemporain toured the
country's major cities under its conductor Pierre Boulez. Boulez, who is
a personable man, appears to regard the interview as a vital means of
advocating contemporary music. In this capacity he is a tireless evan-
gelist. As our conversation continued, various minders came and went
and occasionally attempted to wind up the interview, but Boulez continued patiently to answer my questions and ignore the intruders.

Boulez has always been a polemicist: first as a writer; then as a
conductor, at the climax of which period he was concurrently the chief
conductor of the BBC Symphony Orchestra and of the New York
Philharmonic; now as the head of the Institute for Musical and Acoustic
Research (IRCAM) in Paris. Finding time to compose has not, for
Boulez, always been easy, and yet he remains one of the most significant
voices in post-war music.

AF: You gave up your conducting posts in New York and London
about twelve years ago, but you still seem to be doing a certain amount
of conducting. Is your philosophy of performing really a pedagogical
one? Do you conduct in order to teach audiences?

PB: Not to teach in the sense that I want to bore them, you know.
But certainly I want to bring them music as I understand it—and as I
love it, as a matter of fact. I think that the repertoire that I bring to
audiences is generally a very neglected repertoire: not done very often
and sometimes done badly still. I think if I have a duty, it is to bring
these works under the best conditions possible. So therefore all my
efforts now, when I conduct—which is not very often, except for the
Ensemble InterContemporain—but when I go, for instance, to Chicago
or to Cleveland or New York, that's to bring very specific things; not
to be just part of the season, but to bring something which is missing
in the season generally, let's say.

AF: The standard orchestral repertoire of the 20th century—*Daphnis*

18

and Chloë, The Rite of Spring and so on—you still perform those works every so often; do you find you are at all bored with that repertoire? Do you do it out of a sense of duty or do you still enjoy these works?

PB: I enjoy it now because I don't do it very often. I did *The Rite of Spring* last, I remember, in Los Angeles in March 1987, and I will not do it again before the fall of 1989. So, within two years, that's a pleasure to do it. But that's the thing I cannot really understand about performers, that they repeat always the same thing. I think there is a point where you are dry in front of even the best masterpieces because you have nothing to bring to it. It's just a kind of mechanical pro-duction and I think each time I perform a work I want to discover, maybe, something I've not discovered in it before. For instance, when I do *The Rite of Spring*, I try maybe to refine the balance, to find some correspondence between tempi, to make this work as unified and as convincing as possible. And it brings me joy when I can really be aware of the progress I have made with this work. And the same with *Daphnis and Chloë*, which is a work which is difficult to bring off; not because of its technical difficulty, but because you have a lot of small pieces, and it can quickly be reduced to a set of genre pieces. For me, what is important is to bring the unity and development of this work—like I do, for instance, for *The Firebird*. I choose works always which can really speak to me; if I don't have this relationship with the music, I prefer not to perform.

AF: Your periods of conducting the BBC Symphony Orchestra and the New York Philharmonic: with the benefit of a dozen or so years' hindsight, to what extent do you think you succeeded or failed in your aims?

PB: Well, I think I succeeded in a certain way that now, especially in London, this period is remembered like a kind of golden period. There was, at the head of the BBC at this time, William Glock, with whom I worked very well and I had a very good understanding with the orchestra. Of course, all the pieces we performed were not master-pieces, but I was expecting that. The programs were not conceived one by one, but there was a kind of 'stream' in the season: if you remem-bered a season, you did not remember just a couple of separate perfor-mances, but you remembered, 'Ah yes, that was the season when they did this or emphasised that.' And also there was the diversity I brought to the life of the orchestra: I could divide the orchestra; I brought chamber music; I brought contemporary music. So a lot of repertoire was covered. You know, if you look at programs generally, even the romantic or classical repertoire is much too narrow. I spent a lot of time as music director in London and New York looking at scores which were quite unknown at this time. I did *Lazarus* by Schubert, for instance, and *The Pilgrimage of the Rose* by Schumann. Of course these were not their greatest masterpieces, but I mean generally if you had a museum like our concert life, you would have ten pictures in the museum and nothing else—ten *beautiful* pictures, but that's not enough. You have to have a kind of historical survey. If you have Van Gogh, you have to have also other people of this period, to see the difference and to see how the genius was fed by other people in this period. In music it is exactly the same: if we do masterpieces, we should do also at the same time pieces which are companion pieces. For me that was always the idea behind programs—to bring not only isolated pieces, but to bring a general view of history.

AF: Are you disappointed that the musical life in London has gone back to pretty much what it was before you took up that post?

PB: Well of course you are disappointed when you look at the programs, but I mean there *are* reasons. At least I was spared economic difficulties, because with the BBC, you know, I had not to worry about it. If a concert was not doing very well at the box office, well the next program will do better. But for these orchestras which are living day after day with problems, I can understand that they have to perform war horses to attract audiences. But at the same time there's a kind of vicious circle here, because I have spoken quite a lot with some musicians with these orchestras in London and they are really not very satisfied by this type of solution. They would like to do more interesting programs. But I think that more adventurous ideas about programming are progressively invading the so-called 'normal' world. It takes time.

AF: In New York you certainly had economic constraints. Were they a problem for you?

PB: Yes, the New York Philharmonic was not the BBC from this point of view. I knew that if I did too much of that or too much of this it would have been a wrong move, and therefore I had to be very careful with the balance. But I think if you try to please everybody all the time, you don't please anybody . . . in no time at all. The problem with subscription systems is that you feed the people with exactly the same type of menu. A few first performances—but *very* few—mainly standard repertoire with as many soloists as possible—so many pianists, so many violinists. This is what we call 'international cuisine'. You should organise subscription series according to the type of audience you want to reach. You make one series for people who don't want to hear first performances. But there are also people who want to hear new things. I think the future is to be more like an art gallery. You know you don't have Rembrandts and Van Goghs side by side. You have 17th century Flemish, and then French Impressionists, then Van Gogh and so on. But you can also have an exhibition where you put Rembrandt and Van Gogh side by side, you know. It's not forbidden. So with programming you can have distinctive programs and you can have, I would say, 'clashing' programs. I remember I did that in New York with the Rug Concerts, because it was a different type of audience and I could be much more adventurous. I remember I began a concert with a *Brandenburg* concerto and a Mozart flute concerto and finished with Ligeti's *Aventures* and *Nouvelles aventures*. The people were liking that because they were confronted by strong contrasts.

AF: Is there any connection at *all* between *Aventures* and *Nouvelles aventures* and the Mozart flute concerto?

PB: No. Except that the Mozart is a kind of civilisation; you hear it and you absorb it just like that. But with the Ligeti you have a piece where the concert situation is subjected to a very critical point of view. That was interesting. You could also do it with a Bach cantata and the Ligeti.

AF: I know that there was some criticism that while you were Chief Conductor of the BBC Symphony you didn't play very much British music. I know you championed Birtwistle and Bernard Rands . . .

PB: Maxwell Davies.

AF: Yes. In America there was even more criticism from composers that you were not conducting their work with the New York Philharmonic. When you look at new scores, what do you look for? What is it that earns the Boulez stamp of approval?

PB: Well, first, when you are music director in an institution you can't put your taste in the forefront. If some conductors wanted to conduct pieces I did not personally like, it was not at all my function to say no. Audiences cannot read scores; they have to listen to the works to have the possibility of having a judgement. The second thing is that of course I did not want to perform things myself which I was not interested in; I chose scores which I found provocative. When I chose British composers I chose the ones who interested me: Birtwistle, Rands, Maxwell Davies, Sandy Goehr, Justin Connolly . . . quite a lot in fact. But I would not have compromised on that. But Benjamin Britten? I find that is not very important music to me, so why should I have conducted it? There were other conductors, like Colin Davis, who proposed to conduct that music, so I said, 'Do it, please; you will do it much better than I will, because, for me, I don't find any connection with that music.' As a matter of fact, when I was at the BBC, Britten did not need any promotion, but Birtwistle did and so I preferred to conduct that, rather than to be just ecumenical and play everything.

AF: I suppose that as far as the broad international audience is concerned you are perhaps best known as a conductor of the operas of

Wagner and Berg. There's a certain irony here, isn't there? It was you, after all, who suggested that opera houses should be blown up.

PB: I choose to conduct opera under very special circumstances—only when I have the conditions I can really accept for conducting a good performance. First I want to have a good deal of say in choosing the director. I choose very carefully. I worked with Wieland Wagner, I worked with Barrault on the first *Wozzeck* I did, and I worked with Chéreau. And that was it, practically. When I did *Wozzeck* in Paris in 1963 and then *Lulu* in 1979, I knew that this house was not really the best in the world. So I said, okay, in my contract there will be the number of rehearsals, where they take place, how they take place and if these conditions are not respected, then the contract is broken. And believe me, the contract was respected. I had a very bad experience in Frankfurt in 1966. We did *Wozzeck* with Wieland Wagner in the spring. Then, after Wieland Wagner died in November 1966, they did a revival of *Wozzeck* in December. But in my contract I had not really thought of this revival and they gave me the worst so-called 'normal conditions': one rehearsal and a half for bringing *Wozzeck* back after eight months. And of course the performance was a disaster. A lot of people who conduct in the opera houses accept conditions which are, for me, impossible.

AF: You are extremely interested in literature and, in your own writings, you make constant references to the visual arts, to Mondrian and Klee and Kandinsky and so on. You've never composed an opera or a music–theatre piece yourself. Do you have any intention of doing so?

PB: Well, I came very close once with Jean Genet, but it did not materialise because Genet did not really write any more after *The Screens*. That was his last play. I knew him quite well and, three or four years ago, I thought I had persuaded him to write again, but it came to nothing. And now he has died, so there is nothing I can do about it. I don't want really to reproduce what [had been] done already; I don't necessarily want the orchestra in the pit, the singers on stage. The mobility which directors like Chéreau, Peter Stein and Peter Brook have brought to the theatre: this does not yet exist in the area of opera, because it is much more difficult—you have to be aware of the acoustical aspect. I've discussed at length with Chéreau my ideas for an opera—I would like very much, for instance, to manoeuvre with time, like these directors have done—you know you have a scene of two minutes, like Bob Wilson did, and then you have a scene of half an hour.

AF: Since *Rituel*, your music seems to have become more direct, more gestural. Are you aiming at a greater simplicity?

PB: I would like to say that the *envelope* is simpler. The contents are not. I like to have a content which is rather intricate, rather complex, because otherwise you cannot hear a work more than two or three times—you've understood everything. I think in my recent works it is true that the first approach is more direct, and the gesture is more obvious, let's say. Take *Notations*, for example. In these short pieces the design is very clear. But if you go inside, you know, you find so many small relationships, the knitting of each element is so tight that it takes quite a lot of time to see what is really there. For me it is a game of appearance and reality.

AF: You've often spoken of the musical work as a labyrinth, and what you're saying about *Notations* seems to tally quite well with that concept. What do you really mean by the labyrinthine nature of art?

PB: A labyrinth has a very strong structure, but at the same time it is a structure that fools you. You think you know where you are going, but you don't know how you're getting there. There are two images: the labyrinth and the spiral. *Répons* is a kind of spiral, and each time I compare that with the museum . . . of Frank Lloyd Wright in New York . . .

AF: The Guggenheim.

PB: The Guggenheim. Which is a spiral. Everybody was telling me that it was beautiful architecture, but not good for exhibitions, and I said I don't agree. You look at a painting and, at the same time, you can see what you have already seen and also what you will look at later. So in this museum you have a strong sense of the past and the future, and yet you are in the present. When you listen to a piece of music I want you to feel there is a strong hand behind you, showing you the direction, and yet you are completely in the dark about where you are going: that's always what I try to do.

AF: How do you feel about a concept like post-modernism? What do you understand by it?

PB: Well, there are two concepts which have a different name but which are precisely the same: that's post-modernism and *transavanguardia*, as they say in Italian in such an inventive way. I find that these people are tired; they are afraid of complications, of complexity, and they say that we cannot communicate with an audience because our music is too complex. Okay, so what are they doing? They are going back to something. For me, that's impossible because history never goes backwards. And when I see people who are writing pseudo-Mahler . . . well, there's enough Mahler for me, I don't need pseudo-Mahler. I compare post-modernism with neo-classicism between the two wars. What remains of neo-classicism? Absolutely nothing. It was, at least, better in Stravinsky's hands, but, even with Stravinsky, if I hear the *Capriccio*, you know I am not really as satisfied with it as with *The Rite of Spring*, because *The Rite of Spring* was a real work, and the *Capriccio* is only a mannerism.

AF: So is there a future for modernism?

PB: I don't see a future for modernism; I don't see a future for post-modernism. You are not modern—you are merely expressing yourself according to the coordinates of your time, and that's not being modern, that's being what you are. All kinds of references, for me, are absolutely useless. If I want to be myself, I don't need references. I want to be myself. Period. I really can't see any interest in going back to a lost paradise. For me there is no paradise and there is no loss—of any kind.

AF: I'm sure there is no hint of nostalgia in this, but you yourself have recently been returning to the past and revising old works. *Notations* is one example, and in London you conducted the premiere of a new version of a piece first heard 40 years ago, *Le visage nuptial*. What's all that about—that rewriting of works?

PB: Oh, that's not nostalgia at all. That's really getting rid of something which was not achieved properly. There are two ways of not achieving a work properly. First there is inadequacy in the writing itself—you know, bad orchestration or inexperienced orchestration—but there is also the possibility that the development of your musical feelings has gone much further than the means of expressing them. With *Le visage nuptial* it was a little bit of both. I first composed it for a chamber ensemble in 1946. Then I was not satisfied by the chamber aspect of it, so I made a version for female chorus and orchestra. It was one of the first big orchestrations that I did—I was inexperienced—and I treated exceptional circumstances as though they were normal: exceptional instrumental registers were handled like normal registers; exceptional difficulties, like normal difficulties. And after a lot of experience with orchestras you see that the exceptional *is* exceptional. You have to have a core of normality—you can go further towards the periphery, but it should be considered the periphery and not normality. I tried to conduct it in 1957—I was not an experienced conductor—and I was not satisfied. And I twice tried to conduct it again and the last time—it was in 1981—I said, 'No, it's not possible. It must be redone completely.' I was not at all satisfied with the piece, and how can I be convincing with an orchestra if I am not convinced myself?

AF: One of the works you're conducting with the Ensemble Inter-Contemporain on this tour is *Dérive*. Along with other pieces such as *Messagesquisses* and *cummings ist der Dichter*, it's part of a group of smaller scale works which you have composed over the last fifteen or so years.

Are these pieces like sketches for the larger works? How do they stand in relation to pieces like *Répons*?

PB: Well, *Dérive* was written for the last Bath Festival organised by William Glock. I was completely involved with *Répons* at the time, so I took some elements of that piece, which I did not use in the final version, and made them into *Dérive*—it is a derivation from the main piece. Also—I don't know when it will be done, but it will be done—I have in mind a kind of succession of *dérives* from different works, a mosaic of small pieces. With *Messagesquisses* it was different. It was for the 70th birthday of Paul Sacher and I used the rhythm of his name [in Morse code] and the letters of his name, and it was one of the first ideas for some places of *Répons*: that was a pre-sketch, let's say, and *Dérive* was really a post-sketch. With *cummings ist der Dichter* I have already done another version—the original is not destroyed, but I want to compose more poems by [e e] cummings and the original group of instruments was not adequate for that, so I changed to a group of 27 musicians which is much more in proportion to ·the chorus. It's also the seed for something in the future.

AF: You've been the head of IRCAM for twelve years. Is it possible to sum up what has been achieved in that time and to give some indication of what the future might hold for that institute?

PB: We have a very important direction which is to make more accessible the interface: man–machine. This involves a higher level of language—language which is more symbolic and less numerical. For instance, if you see a curve it means more to your imagination than figures. Also 'real time' work is important, so that you can modify the field of sound during a performance, as I do in *Répons* for instance. It is an analytical process which is rather complex, but which is instant, and for me this is very important for the future. In the past there are these pieces with tape and always, as a performer, you are a prisoner of the tape—for instance in *Disintégrations* of Tristan Murail you have in your ear a click track with the tempo of the tape and this is very limiting for you as a performer. Now, if the machine can follow the performer, you reverse the situation; if the machine is intelligent or has 'qualities of intelligence' it can even tell when a performer makes a mistake. That is really the direction that I want to push everything. The other thing is the small personal computer which is attached to the big system. Especially with the Mac now, which is very easy to handle, you can make your sketches at home, listen to samplings of sounds and so forth, and then when you have prepared the structure of the music you can go to the main house and just do the work. These kinds of relationships will be much more personal than before. Before you had to work at the central station, so to speak, but now you can have your own specially designed software. This is very important for the future.

AF: Would it be true to say that in your own work as a composer you waited until the technology was sufficiently sophisticated to provide you with a flexible—even a theatrical—capability from machines before you actually dived in and began using them? Prior to IRCAM, with the exception of a couple of early pieces, there's very little evidence of interest on your part in electronic music.

PB: I was always very much interested, but I was *not* interested in the kind of music which could be done with this technology. I had three trial runs, let's say. The first one was in 1948 and the technology was very elementary and did not allow you to do very much. I tried again in 1958 with more sophisticated equipment in Baden-Baden, but it did not go very far. Then there was the studio in Freiburg and in 1970–71 I worked with them for . . . *explosante—fixe* . . .—a work which I will now redo. But I mean it was still very primitive: if you wanted delay, for instance, you had to use tape loops; if you wanted three seconds of delay that was that—to go to one and a half seconds of delay, you had to change the loop. So you were always hitting mechanical conditions which worked against the creative conditions you wanted to impose. So when I spoke to Max Mathews at the Bell Laboratory in New York I understood the importance of the computer, not only to synthesise sound—which was one aspect of it—but to create the technology which was able to respond to the quickness of the mind of today. All things mechanical were avoided. And from this point I was again very interested, because the rapidity and the variety of tasks which could be done by the machine was really corresponding to what I thought.

AF: The Ensemble InterContemporain is one of the foremost contemporary music groups in the world, but it came into being at a time when there was a plethora of early music ensembles, playing on original instruments. How do you feel about the craze for authenticity in classical and baroque music? I know, on the one hand, that you don't like nostalgia and you don't like looking back, but, on the other hand, when you conduct, you are very keen to realise the composer's intentions as exactly as possible.

PB: I think authenticity is necessary so long as you *know* about it, if it is not arbitrarily reconstructed. I have seen so many truths coming out of studying baroque music. What I agree with is balancing the weight of instruments. If you do a choral work of the baroque period, you know very well that there were not big choruses, but that the individuality and agility of the voices was preserved because there was a small number of singers. But if you go on from there to say that Bach had only twelve boys and therefore we must have twelve boys, I say that's stupid, because the conditions a composer has in his time are maybe not the best conditions. And therefore what is authenticity? I am sure the Wagner of 1882 would not have accepted the conditions of Riga in 1841, so to recreate those conditions today in order to be authentic, that I find stupid, really. And that's the limitation of authenticity: the more you try to be authentic, the more you put the music far from real authenticity. There was a big symposium and festival of baroque music for the anniversaries of Bach and Handel in 1985, and I was asked to write an article on what I thought about authenticity. And I said that you will always miss the authenticity of the audience, you cannot recreate the audience of 1710. People who are listening to this music today have the memory of many other things which have come in between. You would have to wash their brains completely if you wanted perfect authenticity, because in 1710 they did not know what we know. From this point of view authenticity is necessarily a failure. But I do agree, for instance, that if you have a continuo of course you cannot play it on a grand piano. And if you play a Mozart concerto on a big Steinway and you have a small orchestra with only two bassoons, you don't hear them in the right proportion. But if you are playing in a big hall, with a lot of strings—for instance, Beethoven's third symphony—well you have to have six horns instead of three, because three horns will have to blow their lungs out of the instruments to match the dynamic level. You have to be careful with this.

AF: But what about matters of style and playing techniques?

PB: In 1955, when *Le marteau sans maître* was performed for the first time, the percussionists were playing the vibraphone and xylophone with two mallets, because it was the technique of the time. Now all percussionists play with four mallets, as you very well know. I cannot imagine in one century from now going back to the authenticity of 1955, because I am much more satisfied with four mallets than with two. If you presented Wagner with the horns of today compared to those of his time, I am sure he would appreciate the sonority, because he was always complaining about his horns and wanting to improve their sonority. It's the same with ornamentation. You see even Rossini complaining about 'these damned singers' and how they ornamented all his melodic lines. And now you cannot find a performance of Mozart or Rossini without all these kinds of flourishes and ornaments, not thinking that the composers were highly irritated by this type of flourish.

AF: You've written extensively about most of the 20th century composers whose music you admire and conduct. But one composer whose work you perform a great deal is Ravel, and you've written practically nothing about him. What attracts you to his music?

PB: I admire his sense of sound. I like very much a part of his work—I don't like much his later pieces; I don't like it when he's too trendy. I mean after the first world war, for instance, when he tried to be . . . [*laughter*] *pre*-modern, let's say, trying to catch the fashion of the moment. (Of course he did it better than anyone else.) I don't find that's terribly deep. But he was a master of his profession and his ability to orchestrate was amazing: most of his orchestral scores are transcriptions of piano works and sometimes it is very hard to believe. If you take *Une barque sur l'océan* from *Miroirs*, for instance, you think that's really a piano piece, but no, it sounds very well for orchestra as well. He had a very acute mind for seeing different aspects of his music. Even in the works I don't like very much, he always has a great sense of sonority. And even in *Boléro*—which is not the piece of his I most adore—the sense of tension achieved only through instrumentation is quite remarkable. From this point of view, he was much cleverer than Debussy was. But I prefer the early Ravel. I like people who are not trying to catch the spirit of the time, but who create the spirit of the time.

Melbourne, March 1988

Richard Meale

Meale in Mullumbimby

Richard Meale

Richard Meale says he dislikes interviews intensely; he is entirely opposed to them. Even—perhaps especially—when his opera *Voss* (1980–86) was making headlines, receiving advance acclaim, trying to live up to an absurd press hype and be the Great Australian Opera, Meale remained quiet. There were interviews with David Malouf (the opera's librettist) and Jim Sharman (its producer)—so many interviews, indeed, that one felt concern for the two of them, constantly trying to find new ways of answering the same questions. But there was barely a word from the composer.

Shortly after the qualified success which *Voss* earned (how could it be anything other than qualified, given the claims of its pre-publicity?), Richard Meale took early retirement from Adelaide University and ploughed his superannuation into a house halfway up the side of a forested valley in Mullumbimby, NSW. Now, most days, he not only has no need to talk to people, he doesn't even have to see them. Meale's days are spent composing—around eight hours' work is normal, followed by dinner in front of the television watching 'something ridiculous'. Towards the end of 1991 audiences of the Australian Opera will hear the fruits of his labours: a second opera with David Malouf entitled *Mer de Glace*.

'Moving to the forest has given me the time to correct and perfect this opera,' says the composer. 'I think it's the most complete piece of Meale I've written and I'd never have been able to achieve it without this isolation. I find working now is sheer pleasure.'

It is nearly a year since I first met Richard Meale and had the temerity to suggest that, as I wasn't a real journalist, he might break his self-imposed silence and give me an interview. Finally, on one of the composer's rare visits to Sydney, I was sitting with him in a restaurant, separated by two plates of Italian food, a bottle of wine and the flashing red recording light of a Walkman. In spite of his misgivings, Meale said he felt 'pretty relaxed'. What I was most anxious to ask him about was the very audible change in style which occurred in his music in the late 1970s and has affected it ever since.

The beginning of Richard Meale's career, along with the rise of Peter Sculthorpe's and Nigel Butterley's careers in the early 1960s, effectively marked the beginning of contemporary music in Australia. For decades the principle influences on this country's composers had been second-rate English organists. In spite of a few sterling individual efforts (perhaps most notably the concert programs of Eugene Goosens), the entire Stravinsky–Schoenberg debate which had dominated 20th century music in Europe had passed us by. By the late 1950s, English pastoralism was on its last legs in Britain, but, thanks to the aforementioned organists, it was still flourishing here.

Meale and his colleagues looked beyond Australia, in the first instance to the European avant-garde of Messiaen, Boulez and Stockhausen. Sculthorpe was not much impressed by what he heard, but Meale went off to explore further (along with David Lumsdaine and Malcolm Williamson, who became expatriates in the process).

Besides his brief European sojourn, Meale went to the United States, where, at the University of California in Los Angeles, his studies in non-Western music included such practical experiences as playing in a Balinese *gamelan*. Unlike Sculthorpe and many of his pupils such as Anne Boyd, the influence of Asian music in Meale's work was less stylistic than structural. Works such as his Basho-inspired, orchestral pieces *Clouds now and then* and *Soon it must die* (1969) owe little to the scales and sonorities of Asia, but gesturally they embrace an Eastern aesthetic.

At UCLA Meale attended a lecture that made a great impression on him. The subject was the music of the developing nations and the composer listened incredulously as Australian music was spoken of in the same breath as the music of Brazil and Cuba. The composers mentioned included Miriam Hyde and Dulcie Holland and due recognition was made of John Antill's *Corroboree*. As Meale says, the man giving the paper had done his homework well; the really shocking thing, for Meale, was the revelation that the speaker's thesis was correct.

By the time Meale came home he was convinced that, musically, Australia was an ill-informed country. Through his own compositions and related activities as a pianist and conductor he set out to rectify the Australian experience of 20th century music.

Those early works were uncompromisingly non-tonal in their harmonic language and serial in their technique. Meale now says that they had to be fierce because they were intended as exemplars. Nevertheless, hearing them today, what is striking about pieces such as *Las Alboradas* (1963), *Homage to García Lorca* (1964), *Nocturnes* (1967) and his homage to Arthur Rimbaud, *Incredible Floridas* (1971), is that they seem distinctly individual utterances. They are linked, not only by their European *non*-musical associations, but also by an intensity of colour and a profound, if troubled, lyricism which is Meale's own. This lyricism is often beneath the music's surface, more latent than blatant, but it is never dormant.

In other words, these works were far more than a simple transplanting of the international avant-garde in antipodean soil, like a musical equivalent of the prickly pear. Meale's music of the 1960s and early 1970s was strong and characterful and, as he now says himself, 'genuinely meant'. It won him a reputation as Australia's most important composer.

Was there, as there has been in the work of some of Meale's colleagues, ever a desire to discover a distinctively Australian voice in his music? How does he stand on this perennial question?

'It's an unavoidable question. And I can say that in a country that boasts of being multi-cultural, how dare we inflict our concept of Australia which has been formed by a white, English-based people? We are trying to dictate what Australia is, and we call ourselves a multi-cultural society. I think it's a big illusion and a sentimental approach, that we have to have an Australian music. I don't think it's eventually a constructive view, because it is false. We are trying to define the thing before it has happened, we are trying to reverse a natural historic process.

'People are looking for an Australian style because there is this horror now of foreigners, which is very scary in a multi-cultural society. But I think it's a very shallow approach to art. Australian music is the result of what is written in this country. If it takes a shape which becomes discernible to others, well why not? But it doesn't have to either. Wouldn't it be interesting if we had a country which had no national musical basis? I mean why not?'

In the late 1970s a change came over Richard Meale, by now a Reader at the University of Adelaide. It began with the orchestral work, *Viridian* (1979). As its title suggests, *Viridian* is an evocation of the kind of rainforest environment which its composer now inhabits. The latent lyricism of Meale's earlier works was now utterly manifest; the lushness of the vegetation which inspired this music was present in every bar of the score. Audiences were surprised, critics were stunned. But, as Meale points out, there is a gap of five years between *Viridian* and his previous work *Evocations*. If the change in his musical direction appeared sudden to listeners, it had been gradual and hard won for the composer himself.

I asked him whether, as other composers have indicated about their own return to tonality, there was any aspect of Meale's stylistic change which was a conscious decision to work with a common musical language. Did he feel, for instance, like Alexander Goehr, that Boulez's continuing investigations into new musical languages were 'looking pretty stupid'? Was Meale making any sort of ideological stand with his change of direction?

'No. Anything I've done is selfish. I mean I'm living out my dream as a person. I loved to write music when I was a child and this has simply been my existence. And what more rewarding existence could you have, as you very well know? I mean I've got no time to sit down and look at my navel till I die and I don't think I'll be interested in it then. I take that back—I did look at my navel once. But what I mean is that if you're writing music or if *I'm* writing music, it's a personal venture. The fact that it has become "of use" is something which gives me a special thrill, because not only have I got a hobby, but I've got a hobby which interests some other people. I write music continuously because I'm obsessive. And because I don't see a composition clearly at the beginning, it's always been an explorative experience. But if I've got any sort of attitude, it's really that of letting anything happen, never to restrict a work, to realise that it can go in a different way than the way you are viewing it. That's why I like to start at the beginning of the piece and work it through, because then I can feel the momentum that is building up behind the piece which, of course, is form; the movement of the piece from one moment in time to the next, I think, is what form really is.

'But the change in style was a question of necessity, of personal necessity. Like someone gets sick of where they've been stuck for a while and so they get up and move.'

Part of the reason for Meale's rejection of serialism and his rediscovery of tonality was surely his long-standing wish to compose the opera *Voss.* Prior to that opera he had written no vocal music since some settings of Stephen Spender in his student days. His Lorca and Rimbaud pieces attest to a deep love of literature, but Meale was simply unable to conceive of effective or even 'singable' vocal lines that fitted his musical idiolect.

Speaking of *Voss* he says that it was clear to him that Laura was 'a diatonic lady' and he adds, simply, that since opera is about people it requires a different kind of music. Meale's wariness of interviews is apparent in his tendency to qualify remarks with phrases such as 'I'm only saying this is how I feel' and his comments on the impossibility of composing atonal vocal music earn a particularly big disclaimer: 'I'm simply saying I couldn't do it.'

So then did Meale's change of style coincide with a desire to use his ears more, to rely less on a systematic approach to composition?

'Oh, yes. And the fact that I'm a product of a great history of music. I mean Monteverdi is a great influence in *Voss:* the static chord and particularly the shift of the chord, which so often is totally expressive. Monteverdi's *Orfeo* has been one of the greatest experiences of my life.'

When Meale made his move to Mullumbimby, he invested in an impressive collection of compact discs. This was partly to thwart and partly to make best use of his isolation, but it also related directly to his intention of rediscovering the classical repertoire, which he knew well, but had lost contact with. Amongst the composers he lists as extremely important to him as an opera composer (besides Monteverdi) are Gershwin, Mussorgsky and Debussy—'they form my tutors in writing opera, and I've added Strauss; I've just been listening to *Die Frau ohne Schatten*'.

Meale's retirement from university teaching was partly due to the change in his own music: he says he felt diffident about imposing his new language on his students, although now, if he were still teaching, he would be less coy about it.

'All I ever tried to do when I was teaching was to keep the students' minds open, not to let them start to parody themselves. You know what I mean, if you write something as a student and it comes off, then you tend to do the same again the next week. I was more concerned with the fact that they needed as much experience as possible, so I tried to create situations where I could divert them [into] thinking another way. I wanted to encourage any sign of curiosity in a student.

'It seems to me there's no necessity to teach a student a particular style or technique in their student years. The best thing they can have is a broad experience and that is my philosophy of teaching. The only other form of teaching that I think is worthwhile is when you get a student to help you copy your work and I think Peter Sculthorpe's been very right in doing that. I think that's the way a student can see how a composer is working, actually see one in action. I didn't do that except in the case of *Voss*, because I was not really sure I should be foisting my musical ideas on to any student. But I'd do it now.'

So Richard Meale, the hard-line serialist, the Australian voice of the 1960s musical avant-garde, the man who, in an ABC radio talk, once agreed so vehemently with Boulez that 'the most elegant solution' to the problem of opera was to bomb the opera houses, is now a committed opera composer; he says he's 'hooked'. Since beginning *Voss* he has composed nothing but opera. And when *Mer de Glace* is complete?

'Well, if David will write another libretto, I'll do *it*. I'd say yes to whatever he did. His librettos are very flexible and they already have a great sense of operatic structure; he knows his opera, he's very sophisticated and he has a great sensitivity to what a libretto should be—he couldn't write an unsingable word. But if he doesn't write another libretto, I don't know what I'm going to do. I'll have to get another one from somewhere.'

Mer de Glace could hardly be more different from *Voss*. It is about the rainy night in Geneva when the Shelleys, Claire Clairmont and Byron assuaged their boredom by writing horror stories. Mary Shelley succeeded rather better than the others, producing the first version of *Frankenstein*. In *Mer de Glace* the characters move in and out of reality, sometimes becoming their own creations: Byron is the monster, Shelley is Frankenstein, Claire Clairmont is the bride and Mary is their manipulator. Meale says that the libretto deals with the question of creation, both in the biblical and artistic senses.

'Certainly the novel reflected aspects of their personal relationships, but I see many levels in the opera. I don't know whether I'm putting these things *into* David's libretto, but I feel they're there. But the opera is also an entertainment, I mean there are dances in it, peasant fertility songs, all those sorts of things which should never appear in an opera as we think of it today: a funeral procession, a wedding—in that sense it's quite outrageous. I've found it very interesting to deal with these set situations and find how I make music which sounds like a group of peasants in no one particular place—I mean I really didn't want to have yodelling, although it's set in Switzerland. So I've tried to create something which suggests folk music, although it isn't.'

Since Meale is living and working in a rainforest, cut off from a good deal of the rest of the world (he can't pick up radio and his television reception is severely limited), with his creative mind dwelling in the 19th century, in a house by Lake Geneva, I wondered whether Meale is much concerned with the issues in today's contemporary music world. The change that has come about in his musical style is certainly something he has in common with many other composers. What about the associated polemic about complexity in music: 'new complexity' versus 'new simplicity'? How does Meale stand on this debate?

'Who cares? Who gives a bum? Music goes about its business *despite* all this and that's why I say it's only in the doing of it that music is of any significance.

'I'm living my life. I have no religious or spiritual belief in music, no sense that "this is right" or "we are developing"—pack of bullshit! You do certain things at certain times and that's all there is to it. The music of Beethoven is as valid as the music of Xenakis—to put it perhaps the wrong way around.

'I do believe today that composers have stupid, ill-informed concepts of "world". Very few of them have much perception of what actually exists; in terms of how we view ourselves in the world, a lot of them are up themselves. That's why things have been very spiteful for a few decades. Instead of writing, performing and living, there's been a considerable amount of soul-searching, resulting in pseudo-philosophy.

'Because it seems that most composers are not very well up on other matters, what they're doing is arithmetic of a very low order and believing that, if they make an analogue with some arithmetic structure, that structure will enhance their work. And then it becomes almost voodoo once you get into that area, and I think composers today are tending to speak in a very primitive fashion about their totems. One of the reasons I've ended up in a forest is because I don't feel in key with a lot of my colleagues today.

'There is no progress in music, there's only change. Change and difference are perfectly adequate words to describe what happens. The practice of art is its existence.'

In spite of a certain disillusion with the conduct of contemporary music, Meale's 'retreat to the forest' (as he refers to it) has principally been to allow him more time to work.

'It's my life and it will be my death. Music is my existence. I've certainly been resentful sometimes because I feel it may have cut me out from a lot of normal living. However, that's the way it is. It seemed to me that by going to Mullumbimby at least I'd have the latter part of my life to explore the urges, the things that are in myself.

'I don't believe in causes so much any more. I don't trust beliefs because it seems they lead to very destructive ends—look at Eastern Europe. Freedom is what I'm advocating and what I've sought for myself; freedom to be. And I think art should be a celebration of freedom.'

Is it possible, however, for art to change anything? Meale is particularly concerned about the plight of Ethiopians, their lack of farming success and the incessant war which is a barrier to any improvement in the famine situation. How can an opera about Byron and the Shelleys alter that sort of situation?

'Well, I hope it does; I hope it changes people. I'm trying to give information in an opera. To me there is a lot of deep meaning in the work because it is a study of creation and existence, summed up by the monster who says, "Why did you make me so ugly?". I mean that's a horrifying question.

'I'm interested in the fact that lives are perhaps unimportant, it's art that goes on. There is one point in the opera where it's said that stories end, but life goes on. And Byron reverses it: "No. It's stories that go on forever."

'I suppose I don't sit down and work out what it all means to me in that opera, but I'm thinking about it—because it's in the music . . . That sounds terrible. That's why I don't like interviews. You start saying a whole lot of rubbish . . . '

Sydney, May 1990

Peter Sculthorpe

As simple as that

Peter Sculthorpe

Peter Sculthorpe is bleary-eyed and gravel-voiced when he opens his front door to me at ten o'clock this Sunday morning. He has been up until 4.30 a.m., he tells me, has drunk and smoked too much, and it's all Ross Edwards' fault. We walk through his house to the airy, light-filled studio in his back garden where quantities of black coffee are consumed as we discuss the composer's impending 60th birthday.

AF: When did you know that you were a composer?

PS: Well, without wanting to give the story of my life, I went to my first piano lesson when I was 7 or 8 and I rushed home and wrote music all week. My piano teacher was furious with me and caned me across the knuckles, saying it was a bad thing to write music. She was probably right. So I then wrote it under the bed-clothes for a year or so, until my mother discovered me and said it was all right. I kept writing music, but I also wrote a lot of poetry and painted. When I was about 12 there was a lot of talk about 'what are you going to do when you grow up?' My father would have liked me to have gone into business; my teachers at school wanted me to be a writer; my mother—being a mother—wanted me to be happy. So ultimately I was forced to decide for myself. I realised that my poetry was like 100th-rate Baudelaire, my painting was like 100th-rate Picasso, and my music was like me, because I wasn't really very interested in other people's music. So my music was my voice. And, when I was about 14, I realised I was going to be a composer when I grew up. As simple as that, really.

AF: What would be the experience of a school student in rural Tasmania at that time? What kind of music were you exposed to?

PS: Well, this was in the 1930s and it was very difficult. I remember once my mother was going to Hobart, and I'd heard about a composer called Debussy, so I asked her to bring back some of his music. She came back with the *Préludes* and this was a wonderful experience. I knew about composers like Schoenberg—mostly this man being reviled in books—but the only work which I could get hold of was *Transfigured Night*, which is not even a 20th century work.

AF: You must have wondered why he was so reviled!

PS: Well, yes. A bit later—during the war—I had a friend in the army in England, and I got him to get me the Krenek *Studies in Counterpoint*, which was one of the first books on twelve-note music. I worked my way through that, but it put me off actually—well, it's a pretty dreadful book—but at least I came to grips with that in my early-to-mid teens. In many ways, looking back, I'm rather glad that I couldn't get hold of music, because it forced me to find my own way; whereas today one can hear music that was written and performed last week, from anywhere in the world, and this must be very confusing for young composers trying to find a direction. I found a direction fairly early, and I realised that it had to be through me—nobody was going to give me the key.

AF: Does that make you a naive artist, do you think? Presumably it did at the age of 12, but do you still feel that your technique is, in the best sense, homespun?

PS: Yes. And I hope that I still have some of the naivety that I had then. Why? Because I suppose I feel it's appropriate for a composer living in this part of the world. We've yet to become a truly civilised nation—we're still at the beginning—and therefore to be a little naive is good.

AF: But the naivety which you aspire to is an aesthetic naivety, rather than a technical one?

PS: Back to being 11 or 12. I remember reading somewhere that, when he'd finished a piece, Debussy would tend to take notes out. So I began to do the same—to take notes out rather than add notes. It *is* an aesthetic naivety. I remember, in the 1960s, going somewhere in a taxi with Richard Meale, and Richard was very excited because he said he had written one page of music containing 60 separate, unrelated events. And I said, 'Well, how fantastic! But I would be as excited as you if I had written one page of music and there was only one event on it and I could get away with it.' I suppose that's why today I'm very sympathetic to minimal composers. I wish I could bring myself to be more minimal, but somehow I can't. I suppose with minimal music I feel often a little let down, because it doesn't get anywhere.

AF: We're talking aesthetics again, aren't we? Because I think I would argue that any good composer tries to keep things as simple as possible; you find the simplest solution for whatever musical question you've asked yourself. And maybe the difference between—who shall we say?—John Adams and Elliott Carter, is that they ask themselves different kinds of questions.

PS: I'm certain, actually, that Elliott Carter finds the simplest solution for him.

AF: So is it the *questing* of the composer which marks him or her out as 'minimal' or 'difficult' or 'neo-romantic' or 'post-modern' or whatever?

PS: Yeah, I think so.

AF: So where does that leave you? What are the questions you pose yourself? What's your quest?

PS: That's difficult. It's all bound up in trying to create my own language and wanting my music to mirror the Australian landscape and trying to make a shape that's reasonably easily assimilated. I think that structures are so important, and mine tend to be very straightforward.

AF: Can we go back earlier in the composition process, and can I ask how a piece starts for you? What comes first? And what excites you, at that early stage, enough to make you want to spend a long time getting a piece right?

PS: In the very first place, there has to be some kind of emotional commitment. When an American doctor phoned me last year wanting to commission *Kakadu*, I said I'd love to do it, but I'm so busy. And he kept putting the money up, and I kept saying, 'Look, it's not money that I want, it's time!' Anyway I felt badly about it—it was to be a birthday present for his wife—so, to be nice to him, I said, 'What is your wife like?' And he said, 'Why, she's the most wonderful person in the whole world.' And there was something about the way that he said it—his commitment and love for her—and I knew at that moment that I had to write the piece. So that was it. I think a composer is a chooser. We need to limit our choices, and the more we limit them, the easier the piece is going to be to write. I knew that Jorge Mester was going to conduct the piece, so I asked him how long he thought it should be. So, 20 minutes. Manny, the man who commissioned it, wanted the piece to have an Australian flavour. Well, I'd always wanted to write a piece called *Kakadu* and this was the opportunity—'Kakadu' would perhaps be one of the few Aboriginal names that Americans would know, because of *Crocodile Dundee* being filmed in Kakadu National Park. In *Port Essington* I used an Aboriginal tune called 'Djilile'—which means 'whistling-duck on a billabong'—and it comes from the Kakadu area. So I used that melody in the piece. And then, because of Manny, I thought I would write a very chromatic melody over the Aboriginal melody, and this would be his voice, speaking tenderly to his wife. These were all examples of me limiting my choices; this is how I go about it. I get my material and then I mess around on paper putting As and Bs and A1s and C1s and B2s and D3s—trying to sort out the shape. Once I've got the shape and all the choices limited, off I go. It's as simple as that. It doesn't always fit the original idea by this stage, but it's something to build upon.

AF: *Kakadu* was a commission, and I suppose most of your music is commissioned. But let's take a hypothetical example where you suddenly want to write a piece for its own sake. What would you start with? Something extra-musical, like landscape? Or a sonority? Instrumentation?

PS: It's more likely to be something to do with a particular person. I've just arranged *The Song of Tailitnama* [1974] for cello and piano, for a recording by David Pereira and David Bollard, and I've had immense pleasure making this arrangement, thinking of the two Davids and the way they would play it. That's what gives me the commitment. In fact, I think it's always the person who inspires the music. Say somebody asked me to arrange the *Song of Tailitnama* for Rostropovich. Well, I don't think I would, because I don't know him and I wouldn't be very committed. But I know David Pereira and we have a good friendship and it's as simple as that really. As you know, writing music is hard work and there has to be some form of emotional involvement, otherwise there are lots of easier things to do.

AF: Do you ever wonder what is the point of composing music? Do you ever feel you'd be better employed as a fire-fighter or a doctor—doing something which is more obviously useful to society?

PS: But I think that writing music is of immense use to society. It is a mirror of society, of a time, of a period. The culture of a country is perhaps its most important aspect. The history of the human race is measured by its art, more than by anything else I can think of. Sometimes I wish I'd become a writer or a painter, because neither writing nor painting takes up the number of hours that composing music occupies. The other thing is that writers and painters are also more easily appreciated by the general public, probably because everyone can write a bit and draw a bit.

AF: Can you account for the reluctance of audiences to accept new musical experiences?

PS: I don't think there's one simple explanation for this. It does concern me that people buy contemporary paintings and read novels which are just published, but listen to Beethoven and Mozart. It seems very odd to me. I can't myself conceive of sitting down and listening to Beethoven and Mozart.

AF: What sort of music do you play at home?

PS: I tend to listen to a lot of Japanese traditional music, Indonesian music, American minimal music and Australian music—Aboriginal music, of course, included. But I don't listen to a great deal of music at all.

AF: What about the western classical tradition? What music do you admire?

PS: Bach, Monteverdi, Victoria, Palestrina . . . and late Stravinsky. And what occurs to me about these composers, taken together with the traditional music I mentioned before, is that they share a concern with faith or belief. I think this is the music which will endure.

AF: But for most concert-goers—always assuming they have the opportunity to hear it in the first place—late Stravinsky is hardly very accessible; neither, perhaps, is Victoria or Palestrina. Are you saying that what is accessible today is not necessarily what is going to be durable?

PS: Yes. In fact I think about that with my own music. I think if one makes it too accessible I don't think it will endure. It would be just like a firework.

AF: What's the attraction of Asian music for you?

PS: Well, I've always been very attracted to all things Asian. When I was a boy, while other people were collecting European objects—if they were collecting anything at all—I was collecting Buddhas. My interest in Asian music came later. Although I'm of European descent, I wanted to write music which reflected the fact that here we are stuck out here in Australia. Looking back, I think I turned to Asia as a surrogate for Australia. Because, at that time—in the 1960s—I couldn't even write a piece and give it an Australian name and feel comfortable; it just didn't feel right. Similarly it didn't feel right then to be using Aboriginal music in the way I now do. So I turned to Asia, and I'm glad I did because it helped me to consolidate my style.

AF: You haven't really explained the attraction of Asia, though. It can't simply have been its proximity to Australia; neither can it simply have been the fact that it was un-European?

PS: There's an Einstein story. They were talking of putting a time capsule into space, and of putting in it the best of the human race. A scientist said to Einstein, 'We want to put some music in the capsule, what should it be?' And Einstein said, 'The music of Bach, of course. Or do you think that would be boasting?' Well, if I were asked the question, I would put in *gagaku*—Japanese court music. I've always regarded this as the greatest music of the race, and I suppose that's why I was pulled in that direction.

AF: You still haven't said why.

PS: Does one have to say why? It's beyond emotion; I find it sublime; it has this extraordinary effect on me.

AF: What about Indonesia?

PS: I've always been attracted to ostinato patterns. It goes back to my early teens and was probably the influence of Stravinsky's *Rite of Spring*. So to discover this extraordinary music of Indonesia—and Bali, especially—with these wonderful interlocking ostinato patterns . . . well, it was natural that I should turn to it.

AF: In your eighth string quartet [1969] you employed patterns derived from Balinese rice pounding. Can explain how you did it?

PS: Yes. In the second movement, the ostinato pattern is taken from a recording of Balinese women pounding rice in a big tub to remove the husks. Even the pitches come from that recording, transposed up an octave for convenience. In the fourth movement I've used another technique which occurs again in rice pounding music. I'll talk in bars—although obviously the Balinese women don't think in these terms. One woman might have a pattern which is five bars long, another might have a pattern which is six bars long and another might have a fifteen-bar pattern. They all begin together, they go out of phase and then come together again after 30 bars. Actually, in the quartet it's 96 bars. In Bali it's more interesting still—and if I'd had more instruments I could have done this—because the men just lie about while the women are pounding rice, and every now and then they tap on the tub with sticks and add an upper decoration to the lower notes of the women. The melody in the middle movement of the quartet is from a very early work that I wrote as a student in Melbourne and I later . . . well I didn't disown it, but just . . .

AF: Filed it.

PS: Yes, put it away in a drawer. But I'd always been fond of the melody, so I harmonised it and gave it to the cello. That movement then dictated the shapes of the first and fifth movements. I've always had a love affair with the cello. Apart from being a frustrated architect, painter, poet and concert pianist, I'm also a frustrated cellist. So that's why the cello opens the piece. It's as simple as that. I keep saying, 'It's as simple as that', but actually when the right idea comes one does recognise it, and it really is 'as simple as that'.

AF: Britten once said that he could recognise no correlation between what he considered his most successful pieces and how easy or difficult they had been to write. Can you see one in your own work? Are your best pieces the ones written at white heat, or those which require a lot of concentrated effort?

PS: I've never really thought about it. I suspect the pieces written at white heat are better. String Quartet No.8 is one of those; it was written with great energy and excitement. Actually there's a connection between that piece and Britten, because it was written for the first Radcliffe Award in England, where, I think, four composers were chosen to compose a work, and a judge was to attend the concert and award a prize for the best piece. And Britten was the judge. I thought he was cowardly, because he gave us all equal first prize. I might add that, of the four pieces, it is mine which keeps going. Speaking of Britten, people have often said to me, 'Who do you prefer, Britten or Tippett?' And I automatically say Tippett. And then, when I think about it, it strikes me that Britten has written so many pieces that I really love, and Tippett has written so few. So why do I prefer Tippett? I think it's because Tippett always aims for the stars and sometimes barely gets off the ground; Britten aims for the moon and gets there. And how much better to aim for the stars and not make it!

AF: This is your 60th birthday year. Have you noticed your music changing recently?

PS: I find, as I get older, that my music is becoming more energetic, which is a bit of a curse. You know, it would be nice if one could write one page of slow music lasting five minutes, but instead I write a page of energetic music which might last five seconds. So life is becoming more difficult in that way, but one has to go with what is happening.

AF: A number of composers one could name, including two that we *have* named—Carter and Tippett—have increased their rates of output rather markedly in their 60s and 70s. You say that your music is becoming more energetic—are you yourself becoming more energetic as you turn 60?

PS: Well, I think I am. I've written more music in the last two months than I would normally write in six months. I don't know what's happening.

AF: Perhaps we all have the wrong idea about retirement ages; perhaps governments ought to rethink this area.

PS: Well, unless one is trying to prove a point. No, *I'm* not, because I'm loving what I'm doing. I can just see into the future that I'm going to be writing more and more. It's as simple as that.

Sydney, February 1989

Kaija Saariaho

Just a composer

Kaija Saariaho

The Finnish composer Kaija Saariaho writes some of the most remarkable music of our time. She is interested in the nature of sound and to that extent now lives in Paris, basing herself at Pierre Boulez's institute for electro-acoustic research, IRCAM. Here she is able to employ some of the most advanced musical technology to aid her control of timbre in a growing series of pieces which involve live instruments in conjunction with electronically altered versions of themselves.

I met Kaija Saariaho at IRCAM at the end of a day's work and we walked across the Place Stravinsky to a little cafe, where we ordered drinks and she told me about her current work on a new piece entitled *Amers*.

'It's a piece for solo cello, eleven instruments and electronics, live and also pre-recorded—what would once have been on tape, but is now on hard disk. It's like a cello concerto, but with three factors. We have constructed a microphone which separately amplifies the individual strings of the cello—it's on the bridge of the instrument, very close to the strings—so I can apply the live electronics very precisely. In the pre-recorded electronic part there are two aspects: one is that I have analysed the cello sound, as I've done before, and I am resynthesising it and modifying it and developing things from that material; the other is that I have also synthesised different bell-like sounds which I am tuning microtonally to a keyboard and producing different textures and glissandi which will blend with the live instruments.'

Saariaho's fascination with sampling instrumental sonorities, analysing them and extracting or modifying timbral elements has become a feature of her work. In *Lichtbogen* (1985–86; for nine instruments and live electronics) she experimented with analyses of string timbres produced by varying intensities of bowing, something which she first tried out in her work for orchestra and tape *Verblendungen* (1982–84).

'It's always these sounds which are related to the string-playing techniques I like, which is to do with bow pressure, going from a very clear, harmonic sound to an extreme amount of pressure with a lot of noise. I record this and analyse little windows producing different results with the harmonics and their amplitudes. After that I proceed very intuitively—I just synthesise the sounds that I like and start building harmonics on them.'

What this enables Saariaho to construct is a musical work which, in the most fundamental sense, aligns timbre and texture with harmony, colour with pitch. She points out that it also gives her 'some reasonable way to use microtonality—it's such a vast field that you must find a limiting factor'.

The German word *Lichtbogen* literally means 'bows of light', which I had always taken to be a delightful pun, given that virtually all the music in the piece proceeds from the range of bow pressures. Kaija Saariaho looks at me a little quizzically when I mention this and says that it had never even occurred to her; the title means 'arcs of light'.

'Yes, I realise that,' I reply, 'but in Italian *arco* also means "bow". Are you sure it's not a pun?'

Sensing my unreasonable disappointment, Saariaho concedes that it might be an unintentional pun.

Because of the composer's abiding interest in timbre, Saariaho's work has earned a reputation for fragility. But one does not have to hear very much of her music to conclude that this is quite unjustified. *Verblendungen*, *Io* (1987; for large ensemble and electronics) and *Nymphea* (1987) for the Kronos String Quartet and electronics all pack considerable dramatic punches.

'This reputation for writing fragile music, I think, comes from *Lichtbogen* which is my most played piece. I work very much with form always, even if, as in *Lichtbogen*, the contrast is not so evident. In *Nymphea* the contrasts are stronger, more dramatic. That's the way I need to push myself, because I have a tendency to work on small details which gives the impression of nice colours and detracts from the structure. If people perceive only the surface, they cannot penetrate further into the music. But also, perhaps, *Nymphea* and *Io* are more traditional in their use of contrast than *Lichtbogen*, and as such more audible right away.'

Saariaho studied at the Sibelius Academy in Helsinki with Paavo Heininen, but, in common with many of her contemporaries including Magnus Lindberg and Esa-Pekka Salonen, she felt the need to break away from what seemed the stifling conservatism of Finnish musical life. She went to Freiburg to complete her studies with Brian Ferneyhough and it is a testament to both pupil and teacher that one would never detect the latter's influence in her music. Indeed the composers with whom Saariaho seems most strongly linked are Ligeti, Xenakis and Penderecki, and particularly their predominantly textural works of the 1960s. I asked whether it was an influence she acknowledged.

'Ligeti, surely. I never studied with him or even really studied his scores, but I liked his music very much when I was a student. Yes, I think they all made wonderful works in the 1960s and 70s.'

Ligeti's music from the late 1970s took a radically different turn, partly under the influence of recordings of Conlon Nancarrow's player-piano music. Ligeti's recent works exhibit rhythmic multi-layering of some complexity, together with a far greater sense of tonal centres. For many composers, Ligeti represents the acceptable face of post-modernism. I asked Saariaho what she felt about the general trend towards working once more with tonality.

'I don't think about it. I feel that I don't choose my style. For me all kinds of quotations are completely impossible. I live and I hear and I see what's around me, and then everything must be filtered through me. It must be my music. It's hard to explain, but there's something quasi-religious about my attitude to music: it must be purely what I believe in—it comes as it is and I cannot choose it. I hope it will evolve and change, and in that sense I understand that Ligeti had to move on; he was very brave and I admire him for it.'

Does this mean that she is unaware of having a style?

'What is style? Is it a collection of bad habits? Sometimes I ask myself—because I love certain instruments and playing techniques—are they still the same for me or have they become merely mannerisms? Should I force myself to do something new?'

Two pieces which do exhibit Saariaho's capacity for change and variety are both studio creations: the radiophonic piece *Stilleben* (1987–88) and the extended tape composition *Maa* (1991).

'*Stilleben* is a piece on its own, because it is radiophonic. It was a big pleasure to work on that piece because I had not been in a studio for some years. In that piece I brought together concrete sounds and live music for the first time, and in that situation it was possible to control their interaction. In *Maa*—which means "earth" or "land"—it was different. Because it was music for the theatre, I included things which were very recognisable, like footsteps. I did less processing and only brought all the sounds together in the last section. *Maa* was rather linear because I had to keep it simple for the dancers and the choreographer. It was for the Finnish National Ballet. There is no storyboard for the piece; the themes were symbolic—things about crossing rivers, opening doors, seeing through. But the choreographer and I were too far apart—I understood her, but her working method is very different from mine; even towards the end she was using a lot of improvisation to find the material, and she became rather uncomfortable with the fixed score.'

If much of Saariaho's early student music consisted of vocal pieces, there has been very little, aside from the Kafka fragments in *Stilleben*, to indicate a continuing interest in the voice. Even in *Stilleben* there is virtually no trace of song as such.

'I haven't found a way to use the voice as I wanted. Last year I wrote a piece for the vocal quartet Electric Phoenix called *Nuits adieux* and I feel I'm getting closer. I like the voice very much, but I feel that using a purely classical singing technique doesn't fit my music. Also to make a singer do things that she or he doesn't want to do—they feel they're destroying their voices and so on—-I don't feel good about that either. Yet there are so many ways of using the voice that I want to do it. In *Nuits adieux* each singer has two microphones, and with the second, hand-held mike, which is only used from time to time, the voice is sent to reverb and the length of the reverb is controlled by the amplitude of the voice: the quieter the voice, the longer the reverb. It works nicely and it brought me closer to what I'm looking for.'

I asked whether Saariaho's exile in Paris meant that she was losing contact with her Finnish roots.

'No. I feel very Finnish. Even if I spent the rest of my life in France I would never consider becoming French. So there must be something Finnish in my music, but I cannot tell what it is—probably you can tell better.'

Does she feel, in common with many female composers, that her gender has ever been a barrier to success in a job which is traditionally associated with men?

'My goal was never especially to succeed, but, yes, in the beginning it was very difficult to do what I wanted to do. Maybe my decision to be a composer was left relatively late because I absolutely lacked any kinds of examples. Mine is a very patriarchal culture, which is strange because Scandinavian countries are very egalitarian. But, until very recent years, in culture, in politics, everywhere you found a wise man in the important position, never a woman. Yes, it was a very big thing, and as a student I didn't really know how to deal with that. Now it's something I have accepted, of course, and it's something which evi- dently will never change.

'For a long time my music was always described as "by a woman"; very many colleagues always gave me this "compliment" which is: "I wouldn't have believed this music was written by a woman." For a long time I must have believed these things too—can a woman really write music which is as good and as structurally powerful as a man's?

'But I also really hate this attitude they have in Germany where if you are a woman your music must be played—all kinds of horrible pieces are played just because they are by women. That's not the way either.'

Many feminist musicologists are interested in the notion that there might be a perceptible difference between music by women and music by men. The composer Anne Boyd has told me that she finds she tends to compose music that is within her own vocal range, and certainly she has written a great deal for the flute. Does Saariaho think much about this?

'No. Not in that way. If we categorised—very generally—bad music written by men and bad music written by women, I'm sure they are bad in different ways. Probably. But with good music it is more difficult—in order for the music to be good, things must have found some kind of balance, otherwise it doesn't work.'

While I had been waiting for Kaija Saariaho to emerge from the lift in IRCAM's entrance lobby, I had bought a new CD sampler of music composed at the Institute during the 1980s. As Saariaho's figure receded across the Place Stravinsky, I ordered another coffee and leafed through the accompanying booklet. There were fourteen composers represented in the anthology, all but one of them men. For each composer there was a brief biographical note, holding to the same format: 'Jonathan Harvey. Composer, born in 1939 . . . '; 'York Höller. Composer, born in 1944 . . . '; 'Tristan Murail. Composer, born in 1947 . . . '; 'Pierre Boulez. Composer, born in 1925 . . . '; 'Kaija Saariaho. Female composer . . . '

Paris, June 1992

Sir Harrison Birtwistle

The reticence of intuition

Sir Harrison Birtwistle

Harrison Birtwistle is a private man. Some people have found him abrasive. But his apparently uncooperative way with interviewers is by no means a pose—Birtwistle has never posed in his life. It is not that Birtwistle means to be unhelpful, it is not even that he doesn't want to talk about his music. On the contrary, he is as helpful as he can possibly be, given that his compositional procedures are so personal, so intuitive that there really are no words for what he does.

There is a story about Birtwistle—in his mid 20s and still an inexperienced composer—being invited by Benjamin Britten to the 1960 Aldeburgh Festival where Britten had organised the first performance of what was effectively the young composer's opus 3. Birtwistle took the train to Suffolk, heard a rehearsal of his piece *Three Sonatas for Nine Instruments*, and requested that it not be played in public. Thirty-one years later, as the distinguished composer-in-residence at the 1991 Aldeburgh Festival, Birtwistle merely commented that the piece had been 'fake Darmstadt'. But the story of *Three Sonatas* is instructive. How many composers of such tender years would have recognised that their piece was a 'fake'? And how many young composers would have had the courage and strength of character to pull out of a prestigious premiere at a major international festival, even if they did believe the piece was not very good? Most would convince themselves that the press reviews and general publicity such a performance would bring would be worth it, irrespective of the intrinsic quality of the music. Even back then, Birtwistle was not like other composers. It is difficult to believe that he has ever in his life made an entrepreneurial phone call or written a self-promoting letter.

I have admired his music for as long as I have known it. I finally caught up with the composer himself in a hotel room in London's Covent Garden. He was leading something of a double life, both aspects a bit public for his taste. As well as being in the middle of his Aldeburgh residency (200 kilometres away), he was also attending a short season of performances of his latest opera *Gawain* at the Royal Opera House.

He had agreed readily enough to the interview when I had spoken to him the previous week at Aldeburgh, almost as though he were resigned to this sort of activity whilst out of hiding (he lives in a remote farmhouse in south-west France), but finding an appropriate time and location for our meeting had proved difficult. Now, in his hotel room on an unusually warm June day, the airconditioning creaked and hummed. I mentioned that I was hoping to use the interview for a radio program, but it seemed it was going to be impossible to do anything about the noise.

'Are you going to hold that microphone?' Birtwistle asked.

'I thought I might,' I replied.

'If you hold it out like that you'll get a stiff arm,' he continued with genuine concern. 'Let me hold it.'

He really was being very friendly, and I had heard so many stories about his usual recalcitrance with interviewers that I handed over the microphone. For the next half an hour I watched as he pointed it at his knee, his arm, his ear and, at one point, came perilously close to scratching his beard with it. Even as I resigned myself to the fact that this was going to be a print piece only, it was difficult to get annoyed. He was not sabotaging the interview deliberately, but he obviously felt ill at ease. He listened patiently to my questions and tried his best to answer them, but his tone of voice remained gently sceptical, and behind his eyes there was a look of slight boredom: as if he were thinking to himself that he had heard these questions before and hadn't been able to come up with proper answers on those occasions either; as if he wanted to be somewhere else.

In spite of being a composer from the first generation of British composers to take seriously the continental move towards serialism, Birtwistle has never been a serialist. Calculation and self-consciousness have seldom played much of a part in his music. When they have, he has been the first to spot them ('fake Darmstadt'), and the piece has bitten the dust.

In recent years commentators have begun to discuss Birtwistle's music as part of a distinctly English musical tradition. His pieces are often slow, invariably brooding, and they tend to resemble a procession through a sonic landscape. They are now often compared to the slow movements of Elgar's symphonies, to Holst's Hardyesque *Egdon Heath*, and especially to the symphonies of Vaughan Williams. I asked him whether he felt a part of that, or any other tradition.

'I don't think you can make a conscious decision about tradition. I mean, you're either of it, or you're not. I don't think you belong to a tradition by aping it. In the end I suppose that tradition is what is created, because what I do now—or what anybody does now—is part of tradition. In that sense, I've never made any conscious attempt to write in a tradition.

'I don't really know whether there's even enough of [an English tradition] to be a part of it. You see, you could ask where does Benjamin

Britten come from—because he was not very interested in the music of Vaughan Williams. But we're talking about Vaughan Williams as if *he* was part of a tradition, and yet he's really the only one isn't he? I was listening to a piece of Bax the other day, and that owes so much to Debussy and to French music . . . I think that tradition's a hard thing to talk about when there isn't a direct lineage. If I say to you: Haydn, Mozart, Beethoven, Mahler, Strauss, Schoenberg—there we know about tradition. But put it another way. If you said: Bach, Haydn—is there a tradition there? I see it as being very different.'

It is a fair point. Tradition in English music did not exist even 100 years ago. Can it ever be invented? What Vaughan Williams did, in lieu of that tradition, was to look for models in the music of Tallis and other Tudor composers. Michael Tippett, a generation later, discovered his own voice through his study of the counterpoint of Orlando Gibbons and the songs of Purcell. To what extent has Birtwistle, a generation on from Tippett, felt the need to dig around in musical archaeology in order to find his voice?

'The only thing I've ever consciously looked at is Tudor music and late medieval music. I became interested in that because I saw that this was a music of a different order, a different way of thinking about things. But I don't know you would be able to listen to my music and think, "Oh, that's what he was interested in". That was the point of departure, but it was never conscious. I mean, after all, we all come from somewhere: we don't invent it for ourselves; we don't come from the moon.'

It should have been clear to me by now that the key concept in discussing Birtwistle's music was its lack of conscious style. But I was anxious to try to understand why his music sounds so elemental, why it seems to have been carved out of large slabs of granite. And I was also distracted by the microphone, which was now pointing at me, not him. I asked him, foolishly, if he was aware of tapping into a kind of primeval *Ur* musical language.

'Yeah, well, maybe there is that. But that's your observation. It's not a conscious thing. I never sit down and think, "Well now I'm going to do this, or now I'm belonging to this or that tradition, or here I'm going to do something that's evolving". That's not part of the creative process for me. I think that it's journalism, or even scholarship if you want to get high-flown about it, and you can observe it after the fact, but before the fact it's certainly not part of what I deal in.'

'What you're saying is that it's none of your business?' I suggested.

'No, it's none of my business. That's right.'

'So how do you feel when you sit down to work?' I continued. 'How do you begin a piece? Do you aim for anything in particular?'

'It's hard to generalise. One thing that I do seek is what I would call a musical foreground—something that speaks to the surface of the piece. It's not two-dimensional. Once you have a foreground, then you have a middle ground and a background—you have a depth, you have something you can go into. That way you can then have complexity. I don't think you can have complexity in a situation where it's all complex, or all thick, because then it's all of the same order, and it's not complex then. I'm interested in a linear complexity, rather than density. That doesn't mean that there's no density in what I do—there's that as well—but there is also the opposite of it.'

I asked whether this interest in a three-dimensional musical work— a work which, as Birtwistle puts it, you can enter—led the composer to write pieces that might be described as processionals?

'Well, it might do. You see there again the processional is a means of understanding, a way into it if you like. But we could say all music is a processional, couldn't we?'

The other term that is often used to describe Birtwistle's musical works—he has used it himself—is the labyrinth. I enquired about the difference between the labyrinth and the processional.

'Well, I think there is a difference, yes. But there again this is observation after the fact. I don't make these decisions in advance. I can't write the program note before the piece. I think some composers could, but I can't do that. When I look at a piece I've finished, my observations would be just like I was looking at anybody else's music. And then I could take things out of it which maybe I didn't put in, or I didn't put in consciously.

'You see, I think the problem of talking about creativity is that there's always this idea that the creator is absolutely in control and can answer everything all the way down the line. I don't think that's so. I think you're in control of a certain number of things, and there are also things which happen, which are not accidents, they're things which are thrown up by context. It's a bit like making two buildings. You build one here and another one 200 yards down. And they obey certain principles, but what we didn't take into consideration is the space between the two buildings, and what's going to be a view from, say, a mile away—we didn't consider those things.

'I sort of create, if you like, an imaginary "auralscape". And then I move into it and I discover things in it that I didn't imagine.'

Is he ever surprised by what he discovers?

'I'm always surprised how they speak in time, how things relate over a period of time. Take *Melencolia I* [1976; for clarinet, harp and double string orchestra], you see I was very surprised by that because that's a pretty radical piece in a way. If someone said "write a piece that slow which lasts nearly half an hour", you'd think, well, can you contain that span? Well, I was very surprised that it didn't seem like that somehow. It didn't seem to last half an hour. It didn't to me, anyway.'

'Do you know in advance how long a piece is going to be?' I asked. 'Is it one of the things you plan?'

'No. No, I've no idea. I don't have any plans. I don't do any pre-composition at all. I start writing and when I have a context, when there's something on the page and I can see the first building block, then I can see what I can do with it. And sometimes I rub it out—I cross the beginning out—so you don't know where the music's been generated from.'

This I found faintly staggering. It is because, almost more than any composer I can think of, Birtwistle's pieces have a monolithic quality. Considerable change takes place as the music advances, but it is as though the listener—like the composer—has entered the piece. It is like being in a landscape or a large building and wandering around it, inspecting it from different angles, walking up to things and looking at them closely, then catching sight, from the corner of one's eye, of something in the distance.

I was elaborating thus when I became aware of the grin which had begun to form on Birtwistle's face. 'Yeah, so what's the question?'

'Well, isn't it extremely difficult,' I hazarded, 'to construct a piece— particularly a large piece—if you haven't made any plans?'

'Oh no. It makes it easier. Because I have at one time tried to do this thing of planning pieces beforehand, but then what happens when you come to the crossroads and you're supposed to go this way, but that way looks a bit nicer? What do you do?'

'I'd go the nicer way,' I replied.

'Yeah, that's right. And that's what I do. And that's why I've learned not to have any pre-composition, because then I become the victim of it, I become the slave to it, and that's not the way I find very productive. It's like making methods of composition outside a piece. Like how you make pitches work. I don't do that any more. I've found there are certain combinations of notes that I like, and I could never find them by other means. And so simply improvising them on the piano, and finding their correct spacing, and then subjecting them to analysis to find out if there's any logic to them and finding ways of making them proliferate is much more interesting. Otherwise it's academic isn't it?'

A good example of a monolithic work is the new opera, *Gawain* (1991), based on the anonymous medieval English epic poem 'Sir Gawain and the Green Knight'. There is a labyrinthine complexity about the score—particularly the orchestral music—and it lasts three and a half hours. It has already been compared to Wagner, but presumably Wagner is not a conscious model.

'I won't ask whether it's consciously Wagnerian,' I said.

'Go on. Ask me,' he encouraged.

'Well, is it consciously Wagnerian?'

'I don't know what you mean.'

'In its time-scale.'

'It's a long piece: does that make it Wagnerian?'

I tried to elucidate. 'There are long periods where little happens and then there are sudden moments of fast action.'

'That's right.'

'So there's a sense of time being distorted.'

'That's right. Absolutely. And that's why the piece has to be long. One can very easily get into this terrible, Hollywood hour-and-a-half syndrome, where you have to have something happening every five minutes. And that's not what my music's about. I can't reduce every-thing to the expectancy of people's concentration. I'm not responsible for people's concentration problems. A piece must be the right length.

'But having said that, I think *Gawain* has got one or two problems in that area which I intend to have a look at. Because it's a very ambitious project: just to write it, and then to have it rehearsed and performed in eight weeks is asking a lot. I mean it will get right in ten years time or something.'

Recently Birtwistle's name has appeared as director of his music-theatre pieces. Indeed, a new production of his first opera *Punch and Judy* (1967) was staged at the 1991 Aldeburgh Festival in which Birtwistle and Graham Devlin had joint billing as directors. I wondered whether he had taken to directing because of the problems associated with realising an operatic project?

'No. No, I don't direct. I sort of try to point the way, because I do write from a very definite theatrical point of view. And what's happened once or twice in my pieces is that I see that very thing being taken away and replaced by something maybe equally valid, but it's not the reason why I wrote it. I wouldn't want to keep artistic control. Theatre is a collaboration, but you trust that the people you ask to do it will give you *more* than you ask. And they will do things in a very different way, maybe, but they'll produce the effect that you wanted.'

The Aldeburgh *Punch and Judy* was characterised by a distinct move away from the children's puppet show that inspired the opera. In Birtwistle and Devlin's production the action took place in a sort of post-apocalyptic playground; the characters of Punch and his victims were made to seem very human.

'A woman asked me in the street in Aldeburgh, why is it that we laugh when the puppet Punch gets hit on the head, and why is it so violent when it's not a puppet? That's why that transference to the theatre is so important, it's actually making a statement about that. It's saying that there is something inherent in us which enables us to laugh at something which is actually cruel, because it's become sanitised, it's had the humanity taken out of it: and [in our production] we're actually putting it back. I mean it's not exactly *The Silence of the Lambs. . .* '

But there is also a sense in which Birtwistle's opera emphasises the ritual nature of the violence in the Punch and Judy story. And this seems to be the other very important element in Birtwistle's work in general. The ritual is clear enough in the operas and music–theatre works, but it is there in his orchestral and instrumental pieces too. In certain works—for instance, *Verses for Ensembles* (1969) for wind, brass and percussion—players actually get up from time to time and move to different areas of the stage to play. More recently the chamber orchestra work *Secret Theatre* (1984) has asked for the same sort of thing.

'It's to do with things which repeat, really, isn't it? I mean it's a very simple thing, that. I've indulged in pieces in which performers move on the stage. But the ritual aspect of that has always been a by-product of it. The reason I did it initially was to make it seem that *that* music happens here, in *this place*, and it doesn't happen in another place. It's a sort of visual clarification, and I suppose it is ritual if you say that you only do this in this place. That's what happens in *Punch and Judy*: the murders all happen in one place; Choregos only sings in one place and so on.

'Ritual is simply a means of recognising what sorts of things I do. Another thing too is this question of what I call "instrumental role play". Even in the pieces which aren't specifically designed for the theatre, the instruments are like characters, and so consequently they play in certain places. The first time I did it was in *Tragoedia* [1965] which is for string quartet, wind quintet and harp. Well, the string quartet sits on one side of the stage, the wind quintet on the other, and the harp's in the middle. So you already have a sort of ritual thing. And they each have their own music, and the harp is like a mediator, an instrument of punctuation.'

Many people have commented that there seems to be a strong connection between one of Birtwistle's pieces and the next. I asked him about this sense of continuity.

'That's right. Well, there is. I can only agree. I mean there are connections like this: in *Tragoedia* there's the harp and, within the traditional wind quintet of flute, oboe, clarinet, horn and bassoon, there is an odd-man-out which is the horn, because it's a brass instrument. In the string quartet, the odd-man-out is the cello, because the violins and viola have three strings in common and go down a fifth, whereas the cello is actually an octave below—there's an instrument missing really in a string quartet. And so, when I wrote *Meridian* [1971], I took those three instruments—harp, horn and cello—out of the *Tragoedia* context and put them in the new context: the context is different, you see, but the role of the instrument is the same. And then the harp is taken out of *Meridian* and put into *Melencolia I* where it has a similar function.'

I am staggered for the second time. Most composers plan pieces—big pieces, at least—very thoroughly in advance. On the other hand, if their works resemble one another, it is generally only coincidental. With Birtwistle it is the other way around. About the only area of Birtwistle's creativity that seems completely planned is the connections between his works. It is as if each piece is another chapter in one long book. Perhaps a more appropriate simile would be to liken Birtwistle's whole output to one big labyrinth?

'Yes, that's right. That's right. That *is* conscious.'

I asked if he listens to much music: for instance, does he go to concerts?

'No. Well, I know it.' There was a long pause before he continued.

'I can't take a music-lover's attitude to music. I don't feel I need that sort of top-up of music. I mean, I do hear some, but I never buy a ticket and go and hear my annual Bach Passion or whatever. We have a radio, but I've no method of playing tapes or CDs or anything.'

It is not an especially surprising answer. Birtwistle seems completely self-contained, self-sufficient. He makes the highest demands on himself because, ultimately, it is himself he must satisfy.

I leave his hotel feeling more baffled than enlightened, and yet I also feel as though I have just been given an unusually candid interview. And I can't help wondering, as I ensconce myself in the enveloping comfort of the back of a London taxi, how many artists, deep down, feel precisely the same way as Birtwistle about discussing their work. They would rather not do it, they really don't how to talk about it, but, in the interests of good PR, they will invent pithily quotable quotes for their interviewers.

Perhaps if Birtwistle cared more about his audience's concentration problems, perhaps even if he were a 'music-lover', he would be able to regale us with anecdotes and witty one-liners. And perhaps we should be grateful that he can't.

London, June 1991

Steve Reich

Opening and closing doors

Steve Reich

Steve Reich is an enthusiast. I meet him in his office apartment on Broadway and we talk, or rather he talks—very quickly and with considerable focus, clarifying points, cracking jokes, performing for all he's worth. It is easily fifteen minutes before I get an opportunity to ask my second question, and I begin to wonder whether I should simply have sent my tape recorder round in a Yellow cab. But had I done this, I should have missed the show; and the show is so good that Reich could sell tickets for it.

'As a child I took what I would call middle-class piano lessons, and up to the age of 14 the only music that I was aware of was what I would call middle-class favourites: Beethoven's *Fifth*, Schubert's *Unfinished*, the overture to *The Mastersingers* and so on; I also heard Broadway shows and a lot of popular music. It wasn't until the age of 14 that I heard the music that would end up motivating me to become a composer and informing what I did: that was jazz, Bach and Stravinsky—somehow, within a matter of a few months, I'd heard the first *Brandenburg* concerto, *The Rite of Spring* and several Charlie Parker and Miles Davis recordings. It was like in Bluebeard's castle, where he opens the door and takes you into the room that no one's ever seen: in my case the door closed behind me and I've never really come out.'

Reich says he decided that he wanted to be a composer when he was 17, 'but I thought, you know, Mozart was 6, Bartók was 7 and I was over the hill'. After studies in musicology with William Austin at Cornell University, Reich went to Hall Overton, a composer and a protege of Vincent Persichetti (with whom Reich later studied at the Juilliard School) and a colleague of Thelonious Monk. Reich found Overton's broad sympathies very much to his taste. His final composition teacher, at Mills College, Oakland, was Luciano Berio, but by this time (the early 1960s) Reich was beginning to find his own way and he perceived a stark dichotomy in the music he encountered.

'On the one hand there was what we called "paper music": very black with notes; totally beyond the ability of the composer to play; one doubted whether, in fact, the composer heard it in his or her head.

And then there was John Coltrane picking up his saxophone and the music just came out.'

Reich describes his reaction to this dichotomy as 'a moral dilemma'. At Mills College, where he felt obliged to compose twelve-tone music, he refused to invert his rows in the accepted way, or to use their retrogrades or, for that matter, to transpose them.

'I would just repeat the row over and over. By doing this you can create a kind of static harmony not entirely dissimilar to the Webern orchestral Variations, which are very static and intervallically constant and which suggest this kind of world.'

Reich's back-door tonality quickly became a far more consciously rebellious act. Serialism, the composer reasoned, may have been a natural compositional method for people in the 1950s in Europe—it was a post-war response to 19th century German romanticism—but it was a bizarre direction to take for Reich's compatriots 'who were raised on Chuck Berry'. By mid 1963 Reich had completely abandoned the established 'path to the new music' and begun to investigate other areas.

'One, certainly, was the music of John Coltrane, because, after all, in *Africa Brass* and throughout that period, from about 1959–64, Coltrane was playing a lot of music and very few harmonies: sometimes a whole side of an LP on just F. African drumming became known to me through Gunther Schuller, who I heard talking about jazz at a composers' conference in Ojai, California. Schuller was talking about his history of early jazz and he mentioned a book on African music called *Studies in African Music* by A.M. Jones. So I went back to the Bay area, where I was living at the time, and got it out of the library. I had heard African music but it could have been made on the moon—I didn't know how it was put together. So to see in notation overlapping rhythmic patterns put together so that their down-beats do not coincide showed me a radical new way of making music.'

Reich began to employ his interest in the out-of-phase rhythms of African music through his work with tape loops, leading to works such as *It's Gonna Rain* (1965) and *Come Out* (1966) which are now enjoying something of a comeback amongst today's audience for electronic music. At the same time he also continued his investigations of African drumming and these finally took him to Ghana.

'By the time I went to Africa I knew everything I would find, but I wanted to experience it: there were no surprises there, but there was confirmation.'

Hearing Terry Riley's *In C* crystallised for Reich his feelings about harmonic stasis and he moved ever more surely in this direction.

'The person who first worked in this area of harmonic stasis was definitely La Monte Young—there's no question about that. And the second person who worked in this area, who was influenced by La Monte Young, was Terry Riley—there's no question about that either.

And the third person who worked in this area was myself. And through me, who met and influenced Philip Glass in New York, that's really the chain of transmission. Everyone, except the last person on line there, seems to agree with the history.'

Fearing that he may· have to work with tape loops for the rest of his life, Reich became determined to experiment with his phase techniques by using live musicians. The results were pieces such as *Piano Phase* and *Violin Phase* (both 1967), but their composer quickly found the technique he had pioneered in western music to have become something of a dead-end.

'Now I see *Piano Phase* and *Violin Phase* as, if you will, radical *études*—they are *études* very specifically in a musician's sense of tempo and I've heard reports from students over the years that they have served that purpose, so perhaps they do have a long-term function. But after *Drumming* I had had enough of the technique. If anyone else wants to do it, that's fine; I had to move on.'

At this point I note that the interview has been going for half an hour and the word 'minimalism' has yet to be employed by either of us.

'I don't mention that word at all,' Reich says.

So I ask him, aware that I sound like Senator McCarthy, whether, if he isn't a minimalist now, he has ever been a minimalist.

'This is a stock answer I have, but it's a good one: Debussy didn't like being called an Impressionist and Schoenberg didn't like being called an Expressionist. All these terms—impressionism, expressionism, minimalism—were taken from the visual arts and were applied to composers. I can perfectly well understand why Michael Nyman coined the term in about 1970, and I can even sympathise with it; given the possibilities—hypnotic music? trance music?—it could have been a lot worse. But what I really object to is a way of thinking which I think composers have always objected to, and that is that it's my job to write the next piece, and what interests me in the next piece is what I didn't do in the last piece. And if I know I'm a—fill in the blank—then it's as if I've got a box around my imagination. Whenever I find a composer talking about their own work and applying a label, I always say, "Stop that! You're hurting yourself—don't you know that's like a substance abuse?" You can describe a piece of music without having to give it a term. But codifying it is the job of a music historian or a journalist and I have no bones to pick with them—it's simply not *my* job.'

Label or no label, Reich's music made minimal use of pitch in the early 1970s, tending, instead, to explore slowly evolving rhythmic patterns played by homogeneous ensembles of pianos, marimbas, organs or, in *Music for Pieces of Wood* (1973), claves. The essential technique he devised was one whereby rests were systematically replaced by beats, or beats by rests as the texture and dynamic drive of the music increased or diminished. These works still tend to be harmonically very static.

Then towards the end of the 1970s, in works like the *Octet* and the *Counterpoint* series, melody began to appear and before long Reich had accepted his first commissions for orchestral works, making particularly striking use of the different choirs of instruments which comprise the modern symphony orchestra. The last example of his orchestral work was a piece entitled *The Four Sections*.

'Michael Tilson Thomas said, "Why don't you write a concerto for orchestra?" I said, "Michael, please, I don't do that." He said, "No, I mean why don't you break up the orchestra into the choirs like you're always doing and just focus in on it?" I said, "Ah—you got your piece." I think that *The Four Sections* is a very practical piece that can be done easily by orchestras that have a feeling for it.

'But ultimately the feeling I had from working with the orchestra was a little depressing. Here I am spending a year on this piece and the musicians are looking at their watches—they want to get home to Brooklyn. And whether it's me or John Adams or Aaron Copland, it's not "main dish": it's their charity; it's their "do good"; it's their obligation to the living art of our time or some other boring phrase—and you *feel* that. I'm used to working with my own ensemble or the Ensemble InterContemporain or the Schoenberg Ensemble in Holland—where people are pulling at your shirt saying "Hey, man, what have you got for us?" So I find it a bit of a let-down writing for orchestral players who are basically doing any living composer a favour.

'Also I am devoted to the microphone—I absolutely am in love with the microphone—I intend to work with it till the day I'm dead, and anybody who doesn't like it can go to hell! And the orchestras are still treating it like, "Oh my god, he's using a microphone! It's the end of the world!" When I was writing *The Four Sections* I felt like I had one hand tied behind my back. And when I was all through I thought, "Okay, I'm bust. Enough!" I mean, I can do it, but do I really want to?

'And there's another thing, which is probably more important, which is that people are born with certain talents and not others—I don't know any musician who can do everything, or, if they can, they tend to be like Vincent Persichetti—they can do everything, but you don't really care. I feel that if I didn't do *Different Trains*, nobody in the world would ever have done *Different Trains*. Life is short and there are certain things that I feel like obliged to do.'

I suggested to Reich that *Different Trains* (1988) might be seen as a new departure for him, but that it perhaps also represented a return to the voice collage pieces of the 1960s.

'Yes, it's both. It's a line in the sand; it marks the start of something new. But it also reaches back to *It's Gonna Rain* and *Come Out*. *Different Trains* was the opening to a whole body of work of which my new piece, *The Cave*, is a very large step but, I suspect, not the last one. It also opened the door to music–theatre, which I had always written off because I wasn't interested in opera.'

There were two starting-points for *Different Trains*, one technological, the other autobiographical. Reich explains the former.

'These sampling keyboards which you see here in this room: I became aware that they existed. And I felt: this was done for me! It's been showered from heaven in my lap! Now I have no interest in synthesisers, I really don't; I'm not interested in oscillators imitating instruments. But the idea that one could take any sound in the real world and bring it in on the "and" of three of the fifteenth measure, effortlessly, by pressing a key on a keyboard? Ah, now you're talking! So I had this commission for Kronos and decided to use the sampler, but at this stage it was *tabula rasa*, I didn't know what was going to be in the sampler: at first it was going to be Bartók's voice, then it was going to be Wittgenstein's voice, and I finally ended up with what I ended up with.'

The voices in the sampler finally emerged from the second, autobiographical starting point for *Different Trains*, namely the composer's experience as a child during the second world war of being shuttled back and forth between his estranged parents in Los Angeles and New York. At the time of the piece's composition Reich's mind turned to the train journeys which he, as a Jew, might have taken had he lived in Europe during the 1940s. So *Different Trains* employs sampled fragments of recorded interviews with a retired black Pullman porter, with Reich's now elderly nurse (who had accompanied him on these journeys) and with Holocaust survivors. The spoken portion of the work is fully integrated with sound effects (train whistles, air-raid sirens) and three string quartets (one live, two on tape) which transform the speech into melodic snatches. *The Cave* goes a step further by including video tape.

'We went to the Middle East and we recorded Israeli Jews and Palestinian Arabs and we will record Americans, and when they say something you will see them like on television—as the man from Vienna, who is one of the co-commissioners, said: "Ze noos, set to mooseek!"

'The piece is about the cave of Machpelah which appears in Genesis as the burial place that Abraham buys from the Hittites to bury his wife Sarah; later, it's where Abraham himself is buried, and then Isaac his son, Isaac's wife Rebecca, the grandchild Jacob and one of his wives Leah. The probable dates of Abraham are roughly in the middle Bronze Age—about four thousand years ago. Two thousand years later, when Herod was king, around the time of Christ, he erected a huge wall around what was reputed to be Abraham's burial spot. So it was a shrine already two thousand years ago. Several hundred years later the crusaders came and built a Byzantine church on top of Herod's structure, and then in the 12th century the Muslims came and built a mosque on top of the crusaders' church. A typical story of what goes on in the land of Israel.

'So who is this man Abraham? He is not only the character we know from the Bible, who is the beginning of an immaterial, unified

God that you can't see or hear or touch, but who is the creator of all
that we do hear and see and touch—a totally radical idea at this time.
He is also Ibrahim, who is, perhaps, the central figure of the Koran—he
builds the Ka'ba with his son Ishmael, who is the son who is almost
sacrificed, *not* Isaac. So Abraham or Ibrahim has two wives and one of
them, Sarah, is the mother of the Jews and the other, Hagar, is the
mother of the Arabs, and Ishmael is viewed by the Arabs as their
religious, mythical, genetic father and Isaac is looked at in the same
way by the Jews. So you have a very classical dramatic story which is
also the root of a problem which is on the front page of every newspaper
in the world today.

'Now, how to deal with all this? We have a piece in three acts, and
a different group of people would be asked basically the same questions:
Who, for you, is Abraham? Sarah? Hagar? Ishmael? Isaac? In the first act
we ask these questions to Israeli Jews, in the second act to Palestinian
Arabs and in the third act—which really makes the piece—we ask the
questions to Americans: whites, blacks, Christians, feminists, scientists,
artists—people voicing a small bit of the diversity which one could find.
In the first two acts the people answering these questions are fairly well
informed: they care, even if they're secular. What I think we will find in
the third act—we haven't done the interviews yet—is either a lack of
information ("Abraham? You mean Lincoln?") or a total disdain for the
information, which will also call forth different musical techniques.

'The piece will be in French, German and English, and also Hebrew
in the first act and Arabic in the second. There will be singers and
instrumentalists, as well as the recorded voices and, as you can see, I'm
very excited about the various doors that this is opening.'

Steve Reich believes that it is 'unrealistic' to expect performances
of *The Cave* either in Israel or in Arab countries, and he is highly
sceptical about the work's ability to influence the political position.

'I don't believe that political art serves a function and that we must
get it out there at the barricades: I think that's hogwash. *The Threepenny
Opera* had absolutely no effect in stopping the Nazis; *Guernica* is a
masterpiece but it didn't stop Franco or Hitler or Mussolini for two
seconds.'

As Reich shows me out of his apartment and walks me to the
elevator, he says that sometimes he reads interviews in print that have
been reproduced verbatim, complete with ums and ers. 'You won't do
that, will you?' he asks as the lift doors open. I assure him that I won't.

The doors close and I begin my descent. As I walk out onto
Broadway on this chilly Manhattan evening, I try to remember when
Reich even paused for breath during the last two hours, let alone
hesitated.

New York City, December 1991

David Lumsdaine

The silences

David Lumsdaine

When David Lumsdaine returns to Australia, which these days is quite often, he likes to disappear. He and his wife, the composer Nicola LeFanu, head for the bush. I visited him for lunch shortly after he had returned from several weeks four-wheel driving in Kakadu National Park in the Northern Territory.

Lumsdaine left Australia for England in 1953, studying with Mátyás Seiber and Lennox Berkeley, and by the 1960s was a prominent figure in the British, post-Webern avant-garde. Today, he continues to believe that we inhabit post-Webernian times and, when I asked him about the apparent pluralism of a musical world that contains such composers as Philip Glass, Robin Holloway, David Del Tredici and Alfred Schnittke, he replied, 'You're being provocative.' So I changed tack and asked about Lumsdaine's landscape pieces. Did he, I wondered, make any attempt to 'translate' specific locations—such as Salvation Creek—into music?

DL: No, not specific locations. I suppose the idea of landscape music really means two slightly different things for me, and they occasionally overlap. The first is a formal idea. It was something that I explored a great deal throughout the 1960s. It had its roots in structuring a piece through texture, through the use of space. In the 1960s the difficulty was how to structure music without thematicism. Clearly this kind of landscape idea was behind that, but there were lots of other ideas which came spilling out as soon as one took that particular landscape analogy: ideas of perspective; in particular, of being able to move from a broad view of a texture, into the texture itself. And that, of course, was related to the work and studies I was doing with electronic music—to be able to zoom into a texture, to get right inside a sound, to have very slow-moving harmonies, which could sometimes disappear into a texture. And these, in turn, are related to the big rhythmic structures on which all the landscape works were based. I suppose the last of those was *Aria for Edward John Eyre* [1972].

AF: Are these structures like the ones that you find in Messiaen or

70

Carter? Big, slow beats which you can't really hear, but which mark out the progress of the piece?

DL: I don't think so, because my pieces were all hierarchical works, where the structures were subdivisions of one enormous span which broke down into smaller pulse structures. That contrasts very much with the rhythmic structures which I've worked with since the mid 1970s, which have done exactly the opposite—these have all been additive structures. Although the hierarchic structures often *contained* non-hierarchic structures. In a work like *Aria* for instance, the additive structures—all the percussion strokes and so on—are like a secondary geological structure on top of the first.

AF: So your approach to landscape is to make the musical equivalent of a sort of geological cross-section, rather than to paint a portrait of it?

DL: It's an exploration too. But I said there were two aspects to the idea of landscape and the other one is crucial. It also does away with the linear approach to music; you're not going from A to B. That large structure is there, and you can move through it in so many different ways. And breaking away from linear structures has been one of the most important things to me in my composing life. Nowadays, I guess I like to have a surface structure that anyone can listen to in a linear way—the music goes from there to there to there—but I let the connoisseur listen in a non-linear fashion. But then Mozart's like that.

AF: Yes. So are you suggesting that, at one very simple level, every listener makes his or her own piece?

DL: Oh absolutely, yes. That's always been important to me, that my idea of a piece does not dominate it either for the performer or the listener. My program notes, for instance, are usually pretty open.

AF: But the difficulty of perceiving music in a non-linear manner is that music does exist in time. I mean the seconds tick by, and unless you, as the composer, choose to make something come back again, then it's gone.

DL: Now, wait a moment. Let's think of painting. A painter works at the surface of a canvas. Similarly a performer must work in time, taking one breath after another, and, as you say, the seconds tick by. But one of the most magical things about painting for me is that, when you stand in front of a rich painting, you see the surface, but then the surface disappears. The painting transcends its surface. And any kind of rich music, for me, has to transcend that ticking. Time—whatever time is—is the material of music. It's the material of all rhythmic ideas; it's the basis of all pitch ideas. Time—our perception of time. And the whole point for me is to transcend it. And that's why I get so bored with so much minimal music, which insists upon being so many little ticking clocks. The most important thing in music for me is the silences.

AF: But if I, as the listener, go 'into' a piece of music, if I, perhaps, try to 'freeze-frame' it in order to dwell on a particular sonority or moment of harmony, doesn't the music keep moving and leave me behind?

DL: I think one of the clearest things about a piece of music which is going right, is that you don't have to freeze-frame it, because every sonority is going to last the right amount of time. In lasting the right amount of time, it provides a reference point. You understand a particular gesture; there's a break—something else; and then you have a transformation of that original gesture. Those transformations overlay one another, they take you back. The first gesture had to be the right length in order psychically to imbed itself in your experience, and now it's waiting there—there's nothing lost—it's waiting there for you to pick it up when it comes round again, and you understand the transformation on top of that. Likewise, the other transformations throughout a work: they will also be creating dimensions going this way, dimensions going that way, which are also non-linear. We can only hear them in a linear fashion; we can only understand them in a non-linear fashion. That's not a contradiction for me.

AF: You're talking, then, about the role which memory plays in listening to music?

DL: Yes. I'm talking about memory; I'm talking about eternity and timelessness. If you live in the moment, all time is there.

AF: How does the concert hall affect this pretty intense kind of listening which you—at any rate—hope for on the part of your audience?

DL: I've never found it getting in the way, unless it's a particularly dreadful concert. But you mean all the other people, do you?

AF: Yes, and the fact that they may be unwrapping sweeties or dropping their programs on the floor or allowing their digital watches to tell everyone else the time.

DL: Because music is a social art, to a very large extent people can often reinforce each other's listening. Something which I have lived through very intensely, I can often live through even more intensely with others—there's a sharing which goes on. And it's not just the audience. When you have a committed group of performers who are right inside the music . . . they project a performance, but what they're sharing is something behind that performance. But I'd like to go back to one point which lies behind this timeless business. Most young composers aren't aware of this, although by the time you hit 30 I think you've probably had this experience. A new work declares itself to its composer fairly well in advance, and it doesn't declare itself as a linear structure. It's understood, in the first place, as a moment. Your first idea is usually a *donné* which is right outside time in the usual sense of it. A *donné* can be many things: it can be a texture; it.can be a harmony; it can be just a single gesture. All this has got to be drawn out in time. And the funny thing is that at the same time as we get those timeless *donnés*, the very next thing we know is the duration of the piece—you can almost say within three or four minutes—you have that sense of how long this thing will need to breathe. The two things go together.

AF: Can you say how that moment arises when you have been asked for a specific piece? I mean the phone goes, and there's someone on the other end asking you to write a string quartet, preferably about 20 minutes long. How do you get to your initial *donné* from there?

DL: It's never happened for me like that. I can't compose that many works. I'm a slow composer and the works are born very much of their own volition. This isn't to say that I'm not responding to the incredibly exciting input that performers have in my music; performers have been catalysts to most· of my music. But I've always been lucky enough to be able to say, when somebody has asked me to do something, 'Leave it with me and I'll see what happens', or else the request may suddenly fuse with something which has been at the back of my mind. Ninety per cent of the commissions I've done have been like that; they've been happy chance.

AF: Five of your pieces now have the title *Mandala*. Do you think of those pieces as somehow central to your work? And what makes a piece a *Mandala* piece?

DL: None of them was a *Mandala* before it was finished. So I don't know in advance. The most important technical reason is the way in which the pieces have some quite clear central idea—one that will be very obvious to any listener—and the way they transform this, they are, in the most obvious sense, non-linear. They are like the journey out from the centre of a mandala, but they also contain all those random but very rhythmic readings that one makes across the mandala. Those are all nice ideas, but it's almost superficial to describe them that way. The idea of transformation, as I said earlier, is part and parcel of all my music. There's a certain—in the social sense—public aspect to the various *Mandalas*; there's a sharing of intense solitary experi-ences—experiences of meditation—and an invitation, I think, in each case, to a kind of meditation on the part of the audience . . . These answers are very unsatisfactory. They're all quite true, but none of them comes anywhere near the mark of saying why . . . I haven't composed a symphony since I was in my 20s, and, in many ways, the *Mandalas* could be my symphonies—even the chamber pieces. It's both a neutral and an evocative title. I'm saying the same thing again and again, aren't I? But it's beginning to add up. A work like *Aria* is generated in exactly the same way as the *Mandalas* around it, but it isn't one of them, because it has a very specific location and a very specific title.

AF: And a text.

DL: Yes, I can't imagine any of the *Mandalas* with a text. The *Mandalas* are giving something out. It's a generic title whereby I just give you something, and you make what you can of it. It's your exploration totally.

AF: And so are they central to your whole output?

DL:.   I think we have many different kinds of works in which we will discover that we're trying out new ideas and moving to new territory. I could look at my piano works, for instance, and see each one as mapping out a new area that I'm going to explore. One of the reasons that I know my music will be taking a slightly different direction fairly soon is because I can see a solo piano work coming again. So the piano is as central to me as the *Mandala* pieces are, but I've never composed a *Mandala* for solo piano.

AF: Although there's the solo piece *Ruhe sanfte, sanfte ruh'* [1974] which runs through *Mandala 3* [1978].

DL: Yes, that was composed first. *Ruhe sanfte . . .* is composed 'through' the last chorus of the *St Matthew Passion*. *Mandala 3* goes 'through' *Ruhe sanfte . . .*, going 'through' the Bach. However, you don't have to play with those references too much.

AF: I'm trying to think of the other references to old music in your work . . .

DL: Oh, they're everywhere; it never stops. Mine is a magpie music; whatever I've listened to has become a part of me.

AF: You're eclectic.

DL: Very eclectic in the superficial sense. I don't really make references to other music, it's that it surfaces in my music; there are resonances. Works like the *Bagatelles* [1985] are full of resonances of other music—the piece is about listening to other music—and in *A Garden of Earthly Delights* [1992], I can hear so many resonances that I trust that a very literate listener won't be too busy following all the things that they hear. And yet some of those resonances are very important: there are lots of resonances connected with gardens, including one which is quite searing—which I won't give away, but which shocked me when I first heard it. The reason that I prefer 'resonance' to 'reference' is because all my music is very tightly controlled in its material, but sometimes it starts bending in response to what is at the back of my mind, and taking on this shape or that shape. These are resonances of other music; they contain my experience of it. I suppose, in the landscape pieces, this doesn't happen so much; there are really no resonances of other music there.

AF: And yet it's precisely in your landscape works that birdsong is most likely to turn up.

DL: Yes. Those are resonances in themselves. Yes, you're quite right; it's just that the pieces leave the world of art music and enter the world of other musics.

AF: You seem to require of your audience a very concentrated form of listening; you expect or, at least, hope for the kind of attention which Mozart, shall we say, would never have expected—even though Mozart's music, too, clearly benefits from that kind of attention.

DL: I think all you can do is invite an audience to listen, and there will always be people who don't want to listen. But I can remember one of the most important experiences of getting an audience to listen. It was many years ago, at the second or third performance of *Kelly Ground* [1966], and it was being done by Roger Smalley at a BBC Invitation Concert, where it was the only contemporary work in a program which otherwise consisted of 16th and 17th century choral music—one of those lovely combinations of music which the old Invitation Concerts did so well. I should imagine that the majority of the audience had come along to hear the choral music, and here they were slammed into *Kelly*, which requires concentrated listening if anything does.

AF: It's a big piece, too.

DL: It's also not the kind of work which makes it easy for the listener, and it was quite clearly not inviting this non-contemporary music audience to listen to it. The restlessness about five minutes into the piece was beginning to upset me. But it was a beautiful performance by Roger and gradually I became aware that the audience was stilling, and when it came to the last awful strophe of *Kelly*—the very repetitive, hanging strophe—you could have heard a pin drop. So I just hope that people will go with the music. If they don't, too bad!

AF: I know you said earlier that I was being provocative, but the fact remains that we're surrounded by composer colleagues who go out of their way to make it easy for audiences . . .

DL: Oh, are you talking about this accessibility shit? It's totally irrelevant. A person who has to make their music accessible has got no music to make accessible. There's nothing more to say.

AF: When did you know you were a composer?

DL: I never knew a time when I wasn't. But there was no real encouragement because, for all intents and purposes, the idea of a composer did not exist in Australia then. There were people who composed on the side, but there were no professional composers. The one who took it most seriously was John Antill, but even for Antill it was something that he did outside his work for the ABC. I did finally get some encouragement from Gordon Day at Sydney Boys' High, but when I went to the Conservatorium that ceased. In spite of the presence of Eugene Goosens and Raymond Hanson, 99.9 per cent of my colleagues and the same percentage of staff believed that all the music that was going to be performed had been composed, and been composed quite a long time ago. Composing was just not something that happened now. So it wasn't really until I hit England that I felt I wasn't eccentric. I suddenly found myself amongst colleagues of my own age, wanting to explore the same things.

AF: Were you tempted to come back here in the early 1970s, when things had clearly begun to happen?

DL: The 1960s in London were too important to me musically for me to have returned to Australia—there couldn't have been a more exciting place to be. In any case, I would never have returned while Australia was involved in the Vietnam war. But since Whitlam took Australia out in 1972 I have always been open to the idea of returning. I don't know why it hasn't happened. There must be something which tells me that I could be too comfortable in Australia; it always feels right here, in a way that it never does anywhere else, no matter how much I may enjoy other places. But maybe self-exile is a way of sharpening the imagination for some of us.

AF: When you do visit Australia, you invariably disappear somewhere geographically remote for a period of weeks. What does this give you?

DL: It gives me silence. I don't mean literal silence—there are insects, birds, frogs, the sound of wind, the sound of water—but my physical ears can open up to match the way the ears of my imagination open up when I'm composing. There are very few places in Europe where you can find those perspectives of sound. Most of the time we filter sound, just to be able to have a conversation. To be able to throw those filters away is the other side to the imaginative opening up.

AF: What do you think about that question which seems to preoccupy certain people here in Australia: the question of national identity in music?

DL: People who ask this question rarely ask themselves what the question means. It gets so mixed up with wretched ideas about patriotism and nationalism and all that junk. There is a physical fit which I sense in this country; the way one grows up, the way one's experience of the world is shaped in those years is, for me, the most important shaping. Everything else, like Zen Buddhism for instance, is a rediscovery of those things. What's your original face? What's your face before you were born? In that sense I'm Australian; in every other sense I'm a Martian.

AF: I spoke to John Tavener recently, and he spoke about his studies with you, and he said, in passing, 'I don't know whether David Lumsdaine is religious or not'. So I'm going to ask you. Is David Lumsdaine religious?

DL: David Lumsdaine has got no idea.

Sydney, September 1992

Louis Andriessen

Marx and Janet Jackson

Louis Andriessen

It is early summer and early evening, and, as I walk along Keizersgracht, beside one of Amsterdam's major arterial canals, the distant rumbling and the spotting rain suddenly escalate into a thunderstorm of biblical proportions. By the time I have sprinted to Louis Andriessen's front doorbell, I may as well have swum down the canal. Andriessen, who can barely contain his amusement at my bedraggled state, immediately sets about finding towels and a bottle of whisky. There is a ladder in the centre of his open plan kitchen–dining–living room and we climb it to reach the composer's attic studio, where Andriessen sits at his piano, rolling cigarettes. The only sign of technology is an electronic pencil sharpener. As we talk, Armageddon continues outside the window.

Louis Andriessen has been a particularly important figure to composers of my generation because he has offered a tough and uncompromising alternative to post-Webern serialism—one which could never be confused with the sentimentality of neo-romanticism. Former pupils, such as Steve Martland and Michael Smetanin, often write music which strongly suggests the Dutchman's fingerprints on their scores. For Andriessen, it is Stravinsky who points the way in 20th century music. This is apparent not only from Andriessen's dynamically rhythmic music but also from his book, *The Apollonian Clockwork*, written with Elmer Schönberger, which is one of the most stimulating books on music around, and perhaps the best study to date of Stravinsky and his work. And yet there is something of a paradox here, for Andriessen's music carries a strong political message. Was it not Stravinsky who maintained that music cannot express anything but itself?

'It's important to see that statement in its historical context,' Andriessen insists, self-mockingly adding, 'now I sound like an old Marxist—which I am, in fact.

'It's also important to see that he said it at a time when modernism was not as accepted as it is nowadays, and most people thought that the *Lieder* of Schubert—to give one of the best examples—were the highest musical expression. Specifically, Mahler is a composer where, in their perception of the music, people think of non-musical elements a lot. So, in the context of late romanticism this was a powerful and revolutionary statement. Of course, Stravinsky knew very well also that the structure of a certain aria in Bach's *St Matthew Passion*, to take an example, has definitely to do with text. So Stravinsky's expression was polemical. He was very well aware that the structural or liturgical or ritual elements of texts are extremely important for a composer. Also for him. Also for me.'

I point out that this is well and good so far as word setting goes, but, if one removes the verbal text, to what extent *is* it possible for music to express extra-musical meanings?

'I think it does all the time. But it's totally impossible to make a scientific relationship between certain kinds of harmonies, pitches, melodies or rhythms and specific sentiments like jealousy or whatever. I mean jealousy is a good example: we have some idea about what might constitute sad music or funny music, but it would be very difficult to write jealous music. Musical language changes all the time. Bach used musical cliches, if you wish, to say something about "Herr Jesu ist tod"—he would write a special type of music for this—but I won't write that music; even Andrew Lloyd Webber would write different music for that sort of text.'

If J.S. Bach (who features a surprising amount in Andriessen's thinking about music) employed cliches, and if musical language is constantly mutating, then, of course, composers today have their own sets of cliches. I ask Andriessen whether he feels it is necessary to recognise these and avoid them, or, on the contrary, whether they might even be useful in certain circumstances.

'You should certainly try to avoid cliches. However—and this is another reason I would call myself a Stravinskian—I'm fully aware of the fact that all interesting music deals with existing music, and that you always are in a polemical relationship with existing music.'

Not that it really needs mentioning, but I point out to the composer that we are talking here about politics as much as music when we speak of 'polemical relationships'. So Andriessen proposes that we replace 'polemical' with 'dialectical', which, if anything, takes us further into Marxist theory.

'Dialectical is a word I like to use very much. I would say that I deal with Bach in a dialectical manner, because I'm a totally different person and I can't write his music. I use his harmonies sometimes and his attitude towards composing and his ways of thinking about musical material, but in a totally different way, finally, because Bach didn't know Mahler and Bruckner and Schoenberg and all the other guys.

'Apart from Stravinsky, Bach is the main composer I study all the time—every day, in fact. It's very strange and it's getting worse; I'm doing it more and more. At the moment I am writing an opera with Peter Greenaway and I am trying to make a form similar to those which

Bach used in his "operas"—which, of course, are the Passions. What he did in the *St Matthew Passion* has absolutely nothing to do with the psychological operas of the 19th century. What Bach did was to write closed forms—a chorus or an aria or a recitative—in which there is a dramatic development which is actually the beginning of sonata form. I'm sorry, I sound like a professor. I will stop.'

Louis Andriessen was born into a musical family, indeed into a family of composers: his father and grandfather were composers, and so were his uncle and his brother. Andriessen says that he knew he was going to be a composer when he realised that he couldn't do anything else better. He left school at 15 and enrolled at the Hague Conservatory where his father, Hendrik, who was the director of the institution, became his teacher (later, in the early 1960s, he studied with Berio). Being the youngest member of a composing dynasty had certain advantages for Andriessen. He recalls names such as Ravel, Milhaud, Poulenc and Roussel being spoken of over dinner as family friends.

'And I still estimate those composers very highly. There's almost nobody of my generation or younger who loves Roussel, for instance, as I do—they find it naive, I suppose. I have a few friends with whom I can discuss this secret love for Roussel. Very specific friends. And we say to each other, in hushed tones, things like "Have you heard the new recording of the second symphony?" Like porno, almost!'

Throughout his period of study, jazz was a formative influence, especially bebop and cool jazz as played by Charlie Parker and Dizzy Gillespie. Andriessen is also a fan of boogie-woogie and mentions names such as Pete Johnson, Albert Ammons and Pinetop Smith.

'I have been interested in this since I was 15 or 16. I was absolutely not interested in the pop music of the time—Bill Haley and so on. In fact, I must say that the whole white development of pop music doesn't interest me very much. I never liked the Beatles, for instance; I found them quite primitive. I have racist elements in my love of pop music, because as soon as it has to do with soul and black disco, I like it a lot. Even Michael Jackson I like, and especially his sister Janet. That's what's in my car.

'First of all this music is physical. Physicality is lacking in western bourgeois music; it's all in the mind. But in the end I like jazz because it's cold. This is very important: you think bebop is hot, but it's cold music. You can hear this more clearly [by] listening to Miles Davis than to Dizzy Gillespie. But Charlie Parker most of all: he had an enormous distance from his musical material. I call that classicism, in that it's contradictory to romanticism. Romanticism takes you by the hand and leads you to another world; classicism has a certain distance always from the musical object, and that is what interests me in music.'

In the 1960s and 70s many composers wrote pieces which resembled political manifestos, often with revolutionary texts. One thinks of Henze, in particular, but also Bernard Rands, Berio—to an extent—and

Andriessen's compatriot Peter Schat. Apart from Frederic Rzewski, Andriessen is now one of the few prominent composers whose music continues to preach politics in an era when it is unfashionable to take political stands in general, and socialist stands in particular.

'I am sure that most people would agree with me that the rich are becoming richer and the poor are becoming poorer, and that it's wrong—it's definitely wrong. When we all agree on that, we are all communists. Now the way you deal with this sort of problem depends very much on where you live, how old you are and what period of history you're in.'

Andriessen's political commitment shows itself in a number of ways, not least in the texts he chooses to set which range from Plato's *Republic* to Bakunin. Another political act is his refusal, since the 1960s, to write for that bourgeois institution, the symphony orchestra.

'I don't want to write for musicians who don't like my music. Also the public should not be bothered with music they don't like. The way I solved this was to form my own bands, which I think is a very elegant, simple solution. I did it with *De Volharding* [1972] and I did it with *Hoketus* [1975-77].'

These two pieces both lent their names to the ensembles that performed them and, in each case, the ensembles went on to perform other music specially written for them by other composers.

'Because my generation was extremely active in fighting the hegemony of the symphony orchestras over government subsidy, nowadays the situation in Amsterdam has really changed and young composers can write for ten or twelve different ensembles for new music. They're just there. We have our problems, too, but it seems that the situation in Holland, compared to [that in] a lot of other countries, is quite paradise-like.

'Now, at the same time, I am convinced that if you are a composer who wants to write new music which has a polemical relationship with history—as I do—that means that you have to deal with long pieces and large ensembles, because that's the way that music has developed in western bourgeois cultures over the last 100 years. That is a political attitude, of course. So what I decided to do in the 1970s was to write for large ensembles—it's the only way to compare yourself with the development of symphonic culture in the 19th century.

'Now, I'm totally spoiled here because if I'm writing a piece for 50 players, I know who I will get. And if three or four ensembles want to work together to play these big pieces, then I think I have the duty to write those pieces.

'I really don't think I could write for the symphony orchestra. Of course there are some examples of pieces I like: *The Rite of Spring* is an absolute masterpiece for its time which also deals with what I do—the combination of complex chromatic harmony and simple diatonic melodies—which I think is an extremely important opening for the future of musical language. Morton Feldman succeeded with *Coptic Light* in writing a sound for symphony orchestra which I had never heard; I immensely admire pieces like *Trans* and *Inori* of Stockhausen; but now I start hesitating naming pieces for symphony orchestra which I really find innovative.'

Andriessen's large ensembles are generally extremely distinctive in terms of their sonorities. For each piece a new overall sound is invented which is often characterised by choirs of instruments: in *De Staat* (1972–76), for example, there are four women's voices, four oboes, four horns, four trumpets, four trombones, four violas, three electric guitars (one of them a bass guitar) and pairs of pianos and harps; in *De Tijd* (1981) a female chorus is joined by six flutes, three clarinets and six trumpets, pairs of pianos, harps and bass guitars, a Hammond organ, percussion and strings (without cellos). I asked the composer whether his pieces usually take off from these specific sonorities.

'In general I have what I call a vision. *De Tijd* is the best example, because this is one of those pieces which has a very recognisable sonority. The vision in this case concerned the standing still of time, where there is no future and no history, but only an eternal present. I wanted to write a piece about that psychological situation. I gradually got a vague sound—sustained chords in a high register—but it was *very* vague; I must confess to you that I started the piece twice and it didn't work. Finally, having fallen off my bicycle twice, I climbed back on and realised I could handle the longer time structure. So it's not always sound which gets a piece started. A piece like *De Snelheid* [1983], which is about the perception of velocity in music, had more to do with structural elements than with sound.'

Andriessen's current operatic collaboration with film-maker Peter Greenaway is being conducted principally via their fax machines. The faxes leaving the composer's machine are full of exhortations to send no dialogue. The Greenaway/Andriessen opera will consist (as in the Bach Passions) only of closed forms; Andriessen says he is not interested in writing narrative music.

'I think Greenaway is a genius. We should use the word not very often, but I think he's really a genius. He's very fast—I'm fast, but he's twice as fast as I am—but he's also very courteous and very elegant and full of irony. Communication now is very difficult because he works on ten things at the same time, so I get impatient when I don't get replies on my fax machine immediately. But as soon as we are together, we make decisions in a very short time.

'What is exciting for me is that I will be the person to bring him into the theatre. In a film like *Prospero's Books*, it's, for me, very clear that there are too many images; it bursts out of the screen, I think. And I think that it's very important for him to get into the theatre where he has much more space and also more time.'

The opera, whose convoluted plot the composer attempts to explain to me until my eyes glaze over and he gives up, is rich in imagery, involving many different dimensions of activity, including film sequences. I asked Andriessen whether he considered himself to be in some sense post-modern, but his political beliefs would hardly allow that.

'Finally I believe in progress—there is always progress—so I can't be a post-modernist.'

But is it possible to tell what is progressive today? Surely our musical environment is a fin de siècle one? How can we tell what is avant-garde, and does it matter if we can't?

'I don't agree at all. I think we are in a very revolutionary period. What happened in America in the 1970s was extremely avant-garde, particularly the work with limited material and long durations. I think it was so revolutionary that its importance for the future development of music has not yet been recognised in the world at large. I could not have thought of the pieces I have written in the last 20 years without La Monte Young or Terry Riley or Steve Reich or Feldman, to name only a few.

'We suffer a little bit from the fact that the second world war has done a lot of harm to history in general and, specifically, to music. The generation of Boulez and Stockhausen attached too much importance to the second Viennese school. Sure, they wrote masterpieces which will be immortal, but now we can see that the attitude of the Viennese school was essentially 19th century—not only Schoenberg and Berg but also early Webern; and I'm beginning to have my doubts about late Webern too, with the subjective rhythm and romantic *Sehnsucht*. It's all music which deals with 19th century German chromaticism. So I have my doubts about complexity and about quarter-tone music too: as soon as it gets muddy, I'm not interested any more; I think musical statements should be extremely clear.'

Amsterdam, June 1992

John Tavener

'Maybe I'm completely crackers . . .'

John Tavener

A hassock is a small, stuffed cushion that people kneel on to pray. That the little Sussex village at whose railway station one alights in order to visit John Tavener should be called Hassocks seems entirely fitting, and I tell the composer so as we drive away from it in the direction of his home. It is equally apt that the man who greeted me on the platform is very tall and thin, suntanned (to a degree which in ozone-free Australia would make perfect strangers rush up to admonish him), clad all in white, and adorned with heavy metal jewellery, the religious symbolism of which is at once apparent. He also has long, flowing, bleached hair.

Already an established composer, John Tavener was received into the Russian Orthodox church in 1977, since when his music has been exclusively devoted to its cause. More recently, his very distinctive work has attracted a public far larger than that which a contemporary composer usually draws. The commercial success of the Virgin Classics recording of his long work for solo cello and strings—*The Protecting Veil* (1987)—has not only found Tavener's name in the classical best-seller charts, but the composer himself sitting in Tower Records signing copies of the disc.

We leave the blinding midday sunlight to enter a darkened country house bedecked with religious icons and reeking of incense, only to emerge again into the back garden where we make our way to the very centre of a large lawn: the most sun-drenched spot the composer can find (I instantly feel my unprotected, glabrous scalp begin to burn, and, for the next week, people comment on my complexion). At one of the perimeter fences stands a 6-metre high wooden Orthodox cross, as if to ward off the unholy.

I should add, for the record, that in spite of occasional disconcerting references to the Holy Spirit, which I, at any rate, am unused to encountering in musical conversations, Tavener is quite un-precious about his faith. Commenting on some boring and intrusive neighbours, he remarked that he was tempted to erect a second cross overlooking their garden in order to irritate them.

88

I began by suggesting that Tavener's music had always been idio-syncratic and that, in the 1960s and early 70s, this had made him quite impossible to pigeonhole. Today, however, along with composers such as Górecki and Pärt, he appears to be almost a part of a movement which specialises in simple, static, modal harmonic fields, long, arching, elegiac lines, and much repetition.

JT: As far as composing was concerned I *was* alone, but not among other artists. I think particularly of Cecil Collins, who painted only angels and fools, and I think of David Jones, the writer and painter, and I think of Eric Gill, who lived very near here in Ditchling—in so far as they were concerned with, in some way, recovering a holy tradition of working. So I didn't feel a total loner, because I knew that in a sense they were loners as well. Also I spent a great deal of time in Greece with rather like-minded philosophers and poets who had opted out because they'd gone to live on Greek islands because they objected so much to the way in which 20th century art—20th century life in general—had been removed from the sacred and had become totally secular: you know, philosophically based, abstract-based, you-name-it-based. Even back in London in the 1970s, I had heard a piece by Arvo Pärt which was being dismissed by everybody as being a big yawn, but I thought then there was something very extraordinary about that piece.

AF: Did you think of yourself back then as a rebel? What music actually impressed you?

JT: I think I was quite an angry young man back in the 1960s. This was a reaction against the po-faced serialism of Sandy Goehr, Harrison Birtwistle and Maxwell Davies, and those endless improvisations of Cornelius Cardew. The greatest influence in my early days, as far as 20th century music was concerned, was Stravinsky; in particular the *Canticum sacrum*, which I was actually present at in St Mark's, Venice when I was 12.[1] That piece seemed, in twelve minutes, to bring together *organum* and Webern and even Byzantium. I don't know that Stravinsky knew a great deal about Byzantine music, but that piece impressed me tremendously, and my first attempts at actually writing music were direct imitations of the *Canticum sacrum*. I think it's the nearest that a western man could get to writing what I call 'sacred music'.

AF: I read in a copy of the journal *Temenos* from a couple of years ago an article by you in which you quoted Stravinsky on the late music

---

1 Of *Canticum sacrum*, Tavener told Paul Griffiths that he 'must have heard its first performance broadcast from Venice in 1956, when I was 12' (Griffiths, *New Sounds, New Personalities*, Faber 1985, p.106).

of Beethoven. He said, 'Je ne pense pas, j'écoute.' Is this your own attitude to art?

JT: I think there's a line in Dante which says, 'You who have sound intellects, seek out that gnosis and apply it to your arts'—I'm paraphrasing, of course. It's a very Orthodox concept, the idea of the mind going into the heart, so that you pray no longer with the mind—Orthodox monks incline their heads towards their hearts when they pray. That interests me. The heart on its own doesn't interest me; the mind on its own doesn't interest me. It's something the ancients understood and which I think we've lost—Plato certainly understood it. You know, the right notes had to be found before parliament could be opened. You just can't imagine anywhere in the world today where that would happen. It's all become so abstracted: paintings—icons, if you like—have moved out of the church and into the art gallery; music has moved into the concert hall. Art's become so disconnected with divine realities, whereas in Plato's day—or in any *great* civilisation—it was the norm that it was connected with divine realities. I think we live in a culture in ruins, at the end of an epoch. If you asked me what music was going to be like in 50 years' time, I wouldn't have a clue.

AF: Evidently, these are extremely pluralist times—not just artistically, but in virtually all aspects of life. Do you find this an encouraging thing?

JT: I find it a symptom of decay. Messiaen said that music took a wrong turning hundreds of years ago. I can only assume he meant that, with the introduction of the ego in the Renaissance, art became less and less sacred. I mean it may have reached great human heights at the time of Beethoven, but there's nothing sacred in late Beethoven. I know that's very extreme of me, but in so far as Egyptian wall paintings are sacred, icons are sacred, the Taj Mahal is sacred, St Sofia in Constantinople, Chartres cathedral, I can't see that Beethoven is working in that tradition. Beethoven's music may be the most extraordinary human cry ever uttered, but it isn't sacred art.

AF: I'm afraid I'm going to have to ask you to define 'sacred art' for me.

JT: I go back to Dante; it's a kind of secret knowledge—gnosis. It involves a reworking. I would know if I'd produced a work that was truly sacred if you could dig up a 6th century man and he could listen to it and understand it. Whereas if you dug him up and had him listen to most of the music written in the last 300 years, he would make nothing of it at all. I'm talking about a Primordial Tradition, with a capital P and a capital T.

AF: You're saying then really that music—'sacred' music— should be divorced from language. Because this 6th century man also wouldn't understand much of what we're saying to each other—language has changed a lot. And music has changed, perhaps, in a similar way.

JT: But when I compare, let's say, 6th century Byzantine music with something composed in the last 300 or 400 years, I can't . . . It sounds very judgemental of me, but there's no comparison. I have a problem, having been exposed so much to this eastern music, with the simple drone and the fantastic melodic arch which western music doesn't begin to have—it's very short-winded in comparison. Also eastern music has a function; there's nothing abstract about it. I know when I've spent months and months on a Greek island, listening to nothing but Byzantine singing and music of the Sufis, I find it shocking to hear Schumann, for instance.

AF: Is there any western music at all from the last 700 years which you feel close to? Apart from Stravinsky's *Canticum sacrum*?

JT: I feel close to the unaccompanied cello suites of Bach—more than to his religious music. I love *The Magic Flute*; I think there's something very mysterious about that piece. Tchaikovsky, for some extraordinary reason—particularly the ballet music—I think he can't put a note wrong, but I couldn't explain to you why this is. Mussorgsky also. I think that's about it, but I'm being very sweeping.

AF: Well, it was a sweeping question. And do you actually seek out this music, or is it merely important to you when you happen to stumble across it from time to time?

JT: I think it's important when I stumble across it. I might listen to Tchaikovsky to relax. But as I find with almost all western music, it doesn't inspire me to go on doing what I'm doing.

AF: It doesn't speak to you creatively?

JT: That's right. I mean I can see it's beautiful, and I can see why people like it, but what you said is correct—it doesn't speak to me creatively.

AF: Do you go to concerts?

JT: No. I sort of eschew them. Unless it's music of classical India or Byzantine music, which I'm very glad to see happens quite a lot in England.

AF: So, then, returning to Messiaen's remark, what do you do about this wrong turning which was taken at the Renaissance?

JT: I suppose Messiaen felt that we were lumbered with harmony and lumbered with counterpoint. That's how I interpret his statement. He took the view that we just had to get on with it. Perhaps I wonder if it's possible to return. It's not a question of aping a tradition, but of becoming so *at one* with it that when you're thinking in Byzantine tone systems, something new comes through you. But this is aspirational; I can't judge whether it happens in my music or not. I do know that when *The Protecting Veil* was done in Athens recently, a group of monks, who would have been rooted in Byzantine chant, came up to me afterwards and said that although they didn't recognise per se Byzantine music, they recognised the ethos.

AF: All this talk of 'wrong turnings' and going back makes me wonder whether you are after music which has a kind of prelapsarian innocence, and whether this could ever be a genuine possibility.

JT: Perhaps I feel deep down in my very idealistic self that music shouldn't change that much, that it should be an ongoing craft, like icon painting. But there's a great danger in that. I see all the loopholes, and I can see all the people raising their hands against it. The Greek poet Seferis said the danger is that you get a kind of stultification and nothing happening at all. So I realise that I'm treading a very difficult path. It also requires great courage and, perhaps, humility to let go and to say, 'No counterpoint, no harmony; is it possible to return to these simple modes?' I believe that all the modes—Byzantine, Jewish, Muslim, Hindu—I think they all have things in common; they go back to the dawn of civilisation. So, maybe, to write really theophanic music— music coming from God—one has to go that way. Does this all sound mumbo-jumbo to you?

AF: No; but I find it hard to identify with. Most composers would feel that giving up harmony and counterpoint might put them in a bit of a bind.

JT: Yes. Well I find it myself a bit, too. But then the Orthodox church doesn't actually permit them.

AF: You don't teach much any more.

JT: No. I used to, but I don't think I'm a very good teacher. I had a marvellous teacher in David Lumsdaine. I don't know whether he was a religious man or not, but he certainly had a sense of the mystery of music. He would open various doors on 20th century music for me—you know Ligeti, Messiaen, Boulez—but he always said that he thought I would probably close about 90 per cent of them. But he was never dogmatic. I think if I still taught, that I would encourage a student to pursue his own path. I might put my own views across, as I got to know him, and he could either reject them or take something from them. But I wouldn't force my views on my students because, I mean, maybe I'm completely crackers.

AF: Since you've mentioned David Lumsdaine, perhaps we could talk about that period in your life. Your early career had an enormous boost with your dramatic cantata *The Whale*, which was one of those 'overnight successes' in 1968 when you were 24. How did this affect you? Were you able to put the acclaim into context and get on with writing music?

JT: It's difficult to remember. But there's a similar period at the moment with the success of *The Protecting Veil* and a premiere nearly every week. I have to switch off being contemplative and live a slightly different life. I don't say no to interviews. If I'm writing I tend to say no, because I just like to be here and left in my room all day—and all night if I have to be. But obviously I was much younger at the time of *The Whale* and things are different now. For one thing, I've been very ill since then. I had a stroke when I was 30, and last year I nearly died from major heart surgery. And people ask why I'm prolific! I think the fact of death hanging over me makes me write, and I write at a rather frenetic speed once I get started. However, I've given myself two months off because of this very hectic period.

AF: *The Whale* and *Celtic Requiem* [1969], which is a piece from that early period for which I have a particular fondness . . .

JT: So do I; I prefer it to *The Whale*.

AF: These works came to the attention of John Lennon and you were, I think, the first—and probably the last—so-called 'classical' composer to appear on the Apple label.

JT: Yes, I think I was. I knew John Lennon and I knew Ringo Starr. I don't quite know how or why I did, I can't remember now. They must have heard *The Whale* and asked to see me. I already knew Yoko Ono independently. It was those very heady days of the 1960s, where she was doing Cage-like things in theatres, like shining torches into the audience's eyes, and asking people to come up on stage and jump off ladders. She told people to fly and I remember that ambulances had to be called in, because, well, people weren't flying. Anyway, one evening John and Yoko and I met in an American's house in Hereford Square and played each other tapes, and he rang the next day from his car phone and said they wanted to put *The Whale* on Apple, and anything else that I did, basically.

AF: Were you interested in what the Beatles were doing?

JT: Not in the way that Wilfrid Mellers or William Mann were; I mean I didn't think they were the greatest songs since Schubert. I liked some of them. I was more interested in what the Beatles were doing than in what Maxwell Davies and Harrison Birtwistle were doing.

AF: We've mentioned *Celtic Requiem*; we could add, for instance,

Ultimos ritos [1972] and the *Requiem for Father Malachy* [1973]. This is all music that you wrote before you were received into the Orthodox church, and yet, if not overtly religious, it seems to display a fascination with religion.

JT: Yes, I think it does. I tend to think of those pieces as mystical works, and I now react a bit against mysticism, because it's like sniffing around a restaurant without actually going in.

AF: But can't the aroma from a restaurant induce pangs of hunger?

JT: Yes, that's true.

AF: You've said that when you were accepted into the Orthodox church it was like a homecoming.

JT: A homecoming, yes. Well, I'd sort of flirted with the Roman Catholic church and felt very frightened by that—a mixture of fear and horror. Although sacramentally they're very similar, the Orthodox church doesn't have dogma in the way the Catholic church has it; they would say there is no such thing as forbidden fruit, and so you're left with your conscience.

AF: Would you say that you didn't start writing religious music until 1977?

JT: Yes, I probably would say that, except that I'd call it 'sacred music'. I think the contact with icon painting changed me. However beautiful I might find a Renaissance painting of the Nativity, if I look even at a simple 18th century Russian icon . . . well, one I would just look at as a painting, and the other makes me want to venerate it. I think that's the best example I can give of what I think is sacred and what isn't. Sacred art doesn't make a demand on you.

AF: And this is how you see your music?

JT: That's how I'd *like* to see it. That's why I keep calling my pieces 'icons'. Whether you *can* make an icon out of sound I simply don't know.

AF: I was talking to a painter friend of mine the other day, who was lamenting the fact that she had to work in a medium where you see everything all at once. She was wishing that it were possible to do in painting what you are virtually compelled to do in music, which is to reveal one thing at a time. You have the opposite wish.

JT: I suppose I do.

AF: You've spoken of your chamber opera *Mary of Egypt* [1992] as a 'moving icon', and of *The Protecting Veil* as a 'lyrical icon'. Given the literal impossibility of making an icon from music, how do you set about your attempt?

JT: I suppose I limit the palette in the way that an icon painter does; he's only allowed to use primary colours. I use the tone systems of the Russian, Byzantine or Coptic churches, so I work within a framework. In *Mary of Egypt* I collaborated with Mother Thekla, an Orthodox nun. Most people I asked said they wouldn't touch this subject with a barge pole—it's a mixture of sex and asceticism. I knew I wanted a very simple libretto, like a Coptic or Ethiopian icon. When you first look at them, they are like a child's drawings. And Mother Thekla managed to produce this almost childlike libretto—very simple, very spare in its use of words. We wanted all the movement to come out of an icon, as though the icon were 'liquefied'. It is a series of moving icons.

AF: I'm interested by the ascetic/sexual relationship in *Mary of Egypt*. I'm wondering whether your music aspires to a state of ecstasy—perhaps even sexual ecstasy? I don't know very much about Orthodox religion, but there does seem to be a part of it which celebrates human carnality rather more openly than most of the other branches of Christianity.

JT: Yes, you're right. The Fathers of the Orthodox church talk about 'Uncreated Eros'. Nobody really knows what this is, except that it's maybe what existed before the Fall and, by ascetic effort, we have the possibility of transcending the division in all of us. There isn't the same use of imagery that you find in St John of the Cross. In Orthodox monasticism, for example, being a Bride of Christ would be an horrific thought. I asked Mother Thekla if she was a Bride of Christ and she said, 'No such thing; more like a whore of Christ'. So they don't see this in terms of a relationship with God, but it is possible for human relationships to be divinised, or to become as it was before the Fall. Except that we don't really know what that was like. It's seeing the whole of life as a sacrament.

AF: Are you attempting to make converts with your music?

JT: No. I don't want my music to appear didactic at all, or pro-selytising either. For example, I've had a lot of letters about *The Protecting Veil*, and a lot of people saw different things in it, but very few knew that it was a feast in the Russian church commemorating the Mother of God, who appeared with her Protecting Veil in Constantinople in the early 10th century. It doesn't matter to me a damn whether people realise what it's about. What did touch me a great deal was a letter from someone asking, because of the title, whether I was trying in some way to protect the unfashionable concepts of truth and beauty. What matters to me is that, at the moment anyway, people seem to like the music, and that's what stops me from going off to a Greek island to just write and forget about performances and all the rest of it. It's still a very attractive thought, but I think that would be a sin against the Holy Spirit, because I feel I have got to use whatever talent I have and to take it into the marketplace. There was a time when I was seriously wishing that I could be a small-time Bach in the Orthodox church, because if it's going to become a living church in this country, you've got to invent an English tone system; you can't go on using Greek and Russian melodies. If a Greek shipping millionaire paid me a lot of money for doing it, I might be tempted, but it would be a task for the rest of my life, and if I have any task at all, it is to bring what I've learned into the marketplace and to accept the concert hall.

Sussex, July 1992

Ross Edwards

Silencing the bronchitics

Ross Edwards

At the first performances of *Yarrageh*, a nocturne for percussion and orchestra in the Sydney Symphony Orchestra's 1989 series, audiences found themselves sitting in near darkness. The mood of concentration for a new work was remarkable, particularly since the nature of the music was profoundly meditative—even the Sydney Opera House's bronchitic ward was, for once, practically silent. The composer of this music was Ross Edwards and the success of the piece has been an important turning point for him.

Throughout the 1970s, Edwards' work had become increasingly intricate and precise, sometimes austerely brooding and predominantly quiet. His orchestral work of 1973, *Mountain Village in a Clearing Mist*, is typical of this sort of approach. For all the detail inherent in the score, it seems to the listener as though practically nothing happens. This is not a criticism of Edwards' work—on the contrary, one admires the courage of anyone who is prepared to write music of such a static nature for a large audience at an orchestral concert. Some composers may claim that they write for themselves, that they refuse to allow audience expectations to compromise their artistic vision. But if they are being honest, they will admit that they are afraid of the coughers.

Edwards' dislike of the concert hall verges on disapproval. Although a most loyal supporter of his colleagues' work—always to be found in the audience at others' premieres—Edwards, when it is his turn, prefers to dim the lights in an attempt to persuade his listeners that they are anywhere but a large, public auditorium. At the performances of *Yarrageh* he appeared to succeed.

So heartened is Edwards by the reception to the fifteen minute *Yarrageh*, that he is planning another piece, for horn, strings and percussion, cast in much the same contemplative mould. 'I no longer need to be inhibited by people who say, "He's only writing for himself",' Edwards says.

Edwards' meditative music has been called his 'sacred' style, and the composer himself now uses this description. The style was distilled during a long period of creative silence. During the years 1974–76 he hardly composed at all. He was looking for a musical language which was appropriate to him and as he made this search he became far more closely attuned to the sounds of the natural world. This was an antidote to what he now rather disparages as the cliche of the creative artist in the 20th century. In London in 1970 he had found himself writing the densely complex *Monos II*, chain-smoking Gitanes and living on black coffee and Mandrax: 'I finished the piece and thought to myself, that really is enough of that.'

He went to Yorkshire and discovered that the mix of isolation, introspection and self-criticism produced not only greater contemplation, but, specifically, a contemplation of landscape which became very important to him. Then came the silence. And then the insects.

Edwards stresses that his approach to the sounds of insects is very different from Messiaen's treatment of birdsong. The insects in Edwards' work do not wear labels, and neither is there any attempt to reproduce their actual timbres. What fascinates the composer are not only the rhythmic patterns of the insects, nor even the way in which they repeat, so much as the large-scale structures—the patterns that evolve from the simultaneous repetitions of multiple cycles of insect sounds. Edwards calls it 'quirkish periodicity'. Periodicity of one sort or another is characteristic of many different musical traditions and styles—from Indonesian *gamelan* to Stravinsky, from the classical music of India to that of pre-Renaissance Europe.

If this sounds as though Edwards has merely reinvented the wheel, it should be stressed that his method of arrival at 'quirkish periodicity' was idiosyncratic. Edwards has said that he found himself listening to the silences between the sounds. If, at the time, he considered all music to be 'empty rhetoric', he now also discovered a new kind of logic in the sounds of nature.

But then, in the 1980s, something else happened. In 1982 he wrote his Piano Concerto. His original program note for the concerto stressed that this exuberant celebration of modality was a one-off; there would certainly be nothing like this again. But, far from being an isolated curiosity in Edwards' output, the Piano Concerto, in fact, ushered in a new phase. For a few years the older, static music coexisted with the new, rather bustling textures. But slowly the stasis gave way to the bustle and after *Etymalong* for solo piano in 1984 the contemplation seemed to have ceased entirely.

Edwards has always been at pains to point out that his work methods were unchanged; the insect patterns were still there, the music was still based on periodicity. But, as with the serial Schoenberg insisting he was still writing in the same style as *Transfigured Night*, the similarities have not always been apparent to Edwards' listeners.

As Edwards' Piano Concerto has become increasingly popular with the musical public, it has attracted more and more flak from other composers and from critics. Even Edwards himself has criticised it lately.

After the concerto was performed at the London Proms in 1988, the chief critic of the *Times* described it as 'The sort of piece which gives A major a bad name'. Edwards was more shocked than upset by this and other reviews.

I asked him if the return to quiet contemplation in *Yarrageh* was a reaction to this critical mugging.

'I hadn't actually thought about it in that way—it may have had some bearing on it,' he replied.

Clearly Ross Edwards does not see *Yarrageh* as 'an artist's response to just criticism'. Nevertheless, the new work does have an extraordinarily quiet, ritualistic power about it which suggests that it is a product of careful self-scrutiny by its composer. If this is in any way attributable to the comments of the London critics, perhaps it's time our own critics were a little less cautious in their comments.

Sydney, July 1989

Moya Henderson

The unlevel playing-field

Moya Henderson

Moya Henderson's life is particularly full at present. She is doing her best to attend several performances of her work, she is involved in instrument research and development at the CSIRO, and she has just made her first exploratory trip to Uluru in connection with her largest commission to date—from the Australian Opera. On top of all this she has been celebrating her 50th birthday.

On the day I visited her at her home, perched high above Church Point, north of Sydney, she looked totally surprised to see me. In fact, the date had been planned for some time and our conversation that afternoon was punctuated by repeated apologies for having forgotten all about it.

Composers' 50th birthdays are generally seized upon by the media as a topical hook on which to hang broadcasts and articles. In Henderson's case, however, the event passed largely unremarked by radio, television or newspapers. Although she has one of the highest profiles of any female composer in Australia, she is still regarded primarily and, it would seem inescapably, as first and foremost a woman. This presents two difficulties. On the one hand the general public has yet to come to terms with the fact that there are living composers—that some of them might also be women presents a real challenge. On the other hand, there is the more insidious problem of the institutional neglect of creative artists who happen to be women. Both imbalances are slowly being righted, but too slowly for Moya Henderson.

'It's that rotten unlevel playing-field that's the problem,' says Henderson. 'It's still so damned hilly up our end. And discrimination is so deep in the culture that people don't perceive it; they think it is a level playing-field and that the only determinants [of the commissioning and performing of music by women] are those of quality and standards and all of that.'

Henderson's particular complaint concerns the Australian Broadcasting Corporation; more specifically its concert music department's remarkably poor record of commissioning women. But she does not regard the ABC as exceptional in this regard, merely extreme.

'The hidden agenda is status and economic value and marketability. That's where the discrimination comes in, and that is not identified by people who are non-musicians managing these organisations, because they don't understand—and you couldn't expect them to.

'I think the situation could be amended if there were a greater turnover of assessors of compositions at the ABC. I mean, you're always going to have bias—you know what sort of music you like, and I know what I like; that will of course colour our choices, but if they keep changing the likes of you and me, more and more people will get a go. So I think that some sort of policy like that needs to be implemented, where they have a pretty high and rapid turnover of experts deciding on commissions for the ABC, so it isn't in the hands of a couple of people for years and years and years. And I say that for all sorts of entrepreneurial organisations.

'I do think that what we are [in general] currently experiencing could be described as a backlash. Even in the way people speak: a lot of that sexist imagery is back again, and it's hard to believe, because there was a lot of consciousness-raising, and we tried to make people aware of the significance of certain terms, and of how women are made to look silly in advertising and in jokes. But today it's quite flourishing and probably less naive as well, which is a worry. You just hope that all the ground which has been gained is not lost.

'I suppose also as a woman you look for more support from other women. I mean they do make up 50 per cent of the human race. Where are you, girls?'

The formation, last year, of the Australian Women Composers' Network (which is restricted neither to women, nor to composers), has provided a modest national support group, and Henderson is one of the network's more vocal members. But even if the network is modest in size, it has already had one significant success. Letters complaining to senators about the lack of opportunities afforded to women composers resulted in questions being asked in the Upper House. As Henderson says, in a confidential tone, 'I think some ass was kicked.'

Moya Henderson's curriculum vitae begins in 1973, when she was 32. The period before that seems to have been consigned to official oblivion: she was, she says, 'doing time'. And if this conjures up the image of a troublesome miscreant sewing mailbags at Her Majesty's pleasure, Henderson was in fact serving a higher authority.

Her period in the Sydney convent of Sacré Coeur is something she does not talk much about; one detects her feelings on the matter from statements such as: 'In this country, the musical fraternity is just a tiny notch further on from where the Church is in its attitude towards women.'

The recent radiophonic work, *Meditations and Distractions on the Theme of the Singing Nun*, is further evidence of the detachment Henderson now feels from her early life. The piece, which was an ABC entry in 1990 *Prix Italia* and which won an honourable mention from the jury, examines the life and death of Jeannine Deckers, whose 1960s chart-topping song 'Dominique' indirectly led to her suicide. The Dominicans, claiming that Deckers had no entitlements (although she had not taken even her first vows), enjoyed her considerable royalties up until the time she left the order, and then presented her with a tax bill for the total amount. Deckers sank into an alcoholic depression and she and her lover committed suicide together.

Henderson was still 'doing time' when she began her music degree at the University of Queensland. In 1973, after leaving both establishments, she became resident composer to the Australian Opera during its inaugural season at the Sydney Opera House—an appointment she now finds unbelievable (given her comparative lack of experience), but one for which she is nonetheless grateful and which led to her first attempts at music–theatre.

Music–theatre, indeed, was to form Henderson's principal endeavour over the next fifteen years, although she has always worked in a variety of media and, today, rather objects to the label 'theatre composer'. A German Academic Exchange Student grant and a travel grant from the Australian Council for the Arts (as it then was) made it possible for her to take up advanced studies in Cologne, with two of the icons of the 1960 European avant-garde, Karlheinz Stockhausen and Mauricio Kagel. Kagel still remembers her as one of his most stimulating students.

Henderson's period in Germany also uncovered, almost accidentally, what was to become another of her interests. Whilst working on a piece to be performed on Helfried Hagenberg's 'visually spectacular' sculpture consisting of 27 triangles, the composer 'stumbled upon a new sound'. Since that time she has been constantly involved in developing instruments capable of producing a variety of bell sonorities. The alembas, the family of keyboard percussion instruments which Henderson invented, attracted the attention of Sir Charles Mackerras and have subsequently been employed by the Sydney Symphony Orchestra in several works requiring bells, such as Berlioz's *Symphonie fantastique*. Henderson's work in this area continues, with the assistance of the CSIRO, and she is currently discussing the production of a set of bells for Wagner's *Parsifal* with the opera house at Bayreuth.

Returning to Australia at the end of 1976, Henderson received her first Australian commissions and began a critical but affectionate relationship with Australian culture, via instrumental, orchestral and vocal music, that continues today. This might be thought of as a third strand—alongside music–theatre and instrument-building—in her creative life. Although these strands are frequently interwoven, the third is by far the most dominant one. Like Peter Sculthorpe, Barry Conyngham, Anne Boyd and Vincent Plush, Henderson often seeks an Australian identity for her music. This can be judged as much from her titles—a recent piece, celebrating the release from prison of Nelson

Mandela, is called *G'day Africa*—as from the often distinctive sonorities of her work.

The Australianness of Henderson's creative work is itself two-sided. There is the abiding fascination with the nonconformist spirit of white Australia, which can be clearly discerned in works such as *Larrikins Lot* (1982), her orchestral setting of poems by Patrick White in *Six Urban Songs* (1983), and her adaptation, for voice and piano, of lines from Dorothy Hewett's autobiography, *Wild Card* (1991). Running parallel to these works is a series of pieces that celebrate Aboriginal Australia. These range from music inspired by Aboriginal mythology and music— such as *The Dreaming* (1985) for string orchestra and *Waking Up the Flies* (1990) for piano trio—to overtly polemical pieces, such as the piano concerto *Celebration 40 000* composed against (rather than for) Australia's bicentenary.

Indeed, it is tempting to see this work as polemical in more than one way. Although clearly a refusal to participate in the interminable official festivities, *Celebration 40 000* was also composed at a time when the Australian Bicentennial Authority's commissions had been announced and not one had been offered to a woman. Even if only on the most subconscious level, Henderson's music draws a parallel between the position of Aboriginal people in white Australia and that of women in patriarchal Australia.

Music–theatre, white and black Australia (and—who knows?— maybe even bells) all come together in the work that the Australian Opera has commissioned for its 1994 winter season. In common with John Adams' *Nixon in China* and Andrew and Julianne Schultz's *Black River* (which dealt with Aboriginal deaths in police custody), this opera takes as its subject-matter a story that throws stark light on Australian attitudes to many contemporary issues: the story of Lindy Chamberlain.

Lindy is a collaboration with the writer Judith Rodriguez. In conversation with Henderson, the subject elicits, time and again, one of the composer's favourite words: 'passion' (presumably, given the context, in more than one sense). I asked her to what extent the music of this opera would serve theatrical needs.

'Totally. For me it has to be. I don't want people to be thinking of anything other than the story, when they're looking at the opera. Now that isn't to say that there won't be innovation, both in the way we handle the storyline—the way we deal with reality—and also hopefully in the music.

'I've got this driven attitude towards unself-consciousness in music. I think it's a reaction against a lot of the music that happened in the early part of the century, where you're stopping all the time and assessing what you're hearing because there's no flow-through. I want people to get lost in the experience itself. I want them to have the musical sense of time and not to be shunting in and out of "music time" and real time, which is what happens so often when a piece isn't really working. The *listener* becomes self-conscious—I guess that's what I'm trying to say—I don't want the listener to become self-conscious and to sit there looking at the watch and feeling awkward, I don't want the listener to be conscious of composer and librettist, just to be involved in the work. That would be the greatest triumph I think, to succeed on that front.

'I think the power of music and of opera is that you do invest the work with such intensity of emotion and passion and conviction that that's what the audience buys into. I think that unless you actually feel something when you're writing the piece, then there's no way that the audience is going to feel something. It has to be transferred through feeling and passion in the music itself, that's the transmitter. And if I'm not feeling it when I write it, then I don't expect anybody to feel anything when they hear it. I suspect that's not just my experience, but the experience of many composers, but I haven't heard too many of them talking about it.

'Even writing *Wild Card* there were some songs I could never get through without crying. It's Dorothy dealing with the loss of [her] child and how it came about. I've internalised all that, and dealing with it in music tugged at me. . . I suppose if people hate the piece, I'm going to feel a total drongo for saying that.

'But it'll be the same with *Lindy*. For me the most poignant moment is when they finally bring that little matinee jacket back, by which time she has already served two or three years. That's what I will write first, because the whole opera will feed off that moment of deepest poignancy. Of course I don't really know what that moment was like and I don't want to know. Dramatically it is the heart of the story.'

Those who have labelled Henderson a whinger for her frequent complaints about the status of women composers in this country seem to wish to convey a picture of her as negative. 'Bleak' is one recent description of her (which she resents). But no one who knows Moya Henderson could possibly describe her that way. She has a calm air about her—something one might be tempted to describe as serene, were it not for a strong seam of earthy, irreverent humour which lies just beneath the surface.

Amongst her old friends Henderson provokes a fierce loyalty. When I told him I was interviewing her, her colleague Vincent Plush asked if he might be quoted. I'll leave him the final words.

> Moya's music springs from the soil and she's one of the few Australian composers to have made a sensitive and successful translation of Aboriginal culture to create a new kind of music that is essentially and intrinsically Australian. Not incidentally, she has helped us remember and extend the tradition of composition by women in this country, by the strength of her convictions and the range of her magpie musical consciousness.

Church Point, NSW, July 1991

Judith Weir

Seeing both sides

Judith Weir

Scottish composer Judith Weir is extremely busy, but finds the time to talk to me at the office of her London publisher.

AF: In the last few days I've spoken to Louis Andriessen and John Tavener. I asked them both whether they thought we were living in a period in which we were still coming to terms with the musical developments of the first part of the century. Andriessen said that, on the contrary, we are in a fresh, vital period of musical revolution; Tavener said, more or less, that we are witnessing the death throes of civilisation. What do you think?

JW: Oh dear. I have this annoying habit of being able to see both sides of that. I do have a strong feeling that the public for concert music in particular is coming to the end of its willingness to go out into the concert halls. The whole thing will soon be taking place on CDs—and then, of course, there's the battle with the classics. But in a way I personally feel more energy all the time for my own work and that the musical climate suits the kind of music I do—I feel more possibility there. There are now so many sides to be on stylistically that it is becoming an irrelevant way of looking at music.

AF: Do you not think very much about style, then, in your own work?

JW: I would say that that's true.

AF: So how do you begin a piece?

JW: There's a difference between the work I do with stage pieces—where there's a lot of assembling of sources and texts—and a chamber music piece. With chamber music there's this sense that you can start on any particular day and just get going with it. In the end, it's just to do with finding some small musical object, like an interval set or a phrase or something, and I look on my work in composing really as a sort of variation process.

AF: You start at the beginning . . .

JW: . . . and work to the end. That's right. And I probably build up a technique for the piece as I go.

AF: What about something as large scale as A *Night at the Chinese Opera* [1987]? You don't start a full-length opera with only a phrase or an interval.

JW: No, of course. When it comes to opera the text exerts huge organisational demands. It's a problem with any piece, though, that you can do an excessive amount of planning. When I started to compose it was certainly still the era when one could write and think a lot about the structure of the piece divorced from the actual music. So I guess I do quite enjoy just plunging straight in and, maybe, after writing a minute or two, starting again.

AF: So you're finding your way into the piece?

JW: Yes. I often have the feeling—with my own pieces and others— that it's only in the last few minutes that the piece really gets going. And what a pity, because it's really too late then to tear up the first 20 minutes and start again.

AF: The sort of texts with which you're associated are very distinctive. I can't think of many other composers who work either with medieval texts or Chinese ones. Is there a relationship, would you say, between these two?

JW: Well, I wouldn't say there are just those two, because the work with folk literature is also very important. I think in all of these the quality I notice is a sort of flatness about them, an artlessness—definitely a lack of metaphor. I'm not saying for a moment that I disapprove of metaphor, but in setting the kinds of texts I set, they allow space for the music to do what music does, which is usually to complicate things enormously. I once tried to set a bit of the Auden poem, 'He disappeared in the dead of winter . . . '

AF: The one in memory of Yeats.

JW: That's right. And it was a fascinating exercise, but I found that in that text everything is already there; the music was simply getting in its way. Particularly just simple issues like the audibility of the words. You know, in a text like the one I've just mentioned where the sentences are immensely long, even if it weren't such a great text it would still seem very unfair to clutter it further with music. I think there is an enormous interest in metaphor in English writing—from the metaphysical poets onwards, I would say. So in going to these very simple texts I'm looking for something which just tells the bare bones of a story. I don't know if you've come across a wonderful little book which has just been issued of the five Charles Eliot Norton lectures that Calvino was just about to give before he died. In fact the last one wasn't written: it's called *Six Memos for the Next Millennium*, but there are only five. I should have brought it along. There is a wonderful moment where he tells an Italian folk tale and points out what a bold narrative it is. Supposing, for instance, that the story begins: 'A king was worried by a giant one day.' It doesn't tell you anything about the king or the giant; you don't have to wait around before you hear the story. This thing about having to wait for information—a musical setting lasts such a short time to have to sit through all this detail which the music gives anyway.

AF: So you see your role as composer, then, as a provider of metaphor?

JW: In a way, yes. I think the music is providing the interpretive layers of the text.

AF: There's something rather bloody about the texts of *Chinese Opera*, *King Harald's Saga* [1979] and *The Consolations of Scholarship* [1985]. What attracts you to these stories?

JW: Well, obviously I find a strong interest from a narrative point of view in any text that I set, although it's not always immediately obvious to me what the essence of that interest is. Often it's only towards the end that I begin to be able to work that out. Of the texts you have mentioned—and also my piece about El Cid, the Spanish fighter [*Missa Del Cid* (1988)]—I'm interested in the way they describe very violent people in very matter-of-fact ways. It seems to me that an awful lot of the pieces that have been written about war and violence put a gloss of regretfulness on it—I'm thinking of something like Britten's *War Requiem*. Of course I regret war as much as anybody else but I feel that that almost Bob Dylanish way of talking about war has become a kind of cliche, so in some of my pieces I've tried to present this subject matter, not in a raw, violent way, but in a detached way. There's a bit at the end of *Missa Del Cid* where it says, 'In a short time, one thousand three hundred Moors fell dead upon the field. The Cid spent three years taking these towns and conquering Moorish territory, sleeping by day and marching by night.' That kind of football report quality to me is very interesting. It's like that wonderful film about the Holocaust, Claude Lanzmann's *Shoah*, where he doesn't show a single dead body or an atrocity, but he just gives you little measurements for all these gas chambers and so on. So I suppose a lot of my work has been trying to do that.

AF: The playing of multiple characters by one voice—which is another feature of more than one of your pieces—is this a further attempt to distance the listener from the subject of the piece? Is it a Brechtian device?

JW: There's certainly something of that in it. I adore Brecht and I don't apologise for that. It's to do with the actor's art. I have a lot of thoughts about how television has affected our perceptions of characters. You know, sitcoms can show character by simple visual recognition—you get near to the character. Well, if you contrast that with being in a huge Greek amphitheatre, the actors had to work with all sorts of physical and vocal gestures too. I find that making a singer play several characters draws out much more interesting work from them, and they begin to define their characters in much more scientific ways. In the classic operatic production there are stock characters and the singers have rather trivial, anecdotal ways of getting into them. So if a singer is suddenly plunged into *King Harald's Saga* where they have to be about nine characters, they have to think hard about making these characters different people. It's certainly very interesting for me.

AF: And she not only plays nine different people, but she's the *only* singer in this 'grand opera'—indeed the only performer of any sort, because there are no instruments either. Do you think about audiences much?

JW: I have to say that I'm very interested in audiences' reactions. But I don't really think you can start off by taking that into account. It's funny, because often people say that my music is accessible—and I think they mean it as a compliment . . .

AF: I think it depends who's saying it, actually.

JW: Yes, that's true. But I think you're on dangerous ground if you start trying to guess what audiences will like. I've noticed this particularly with *Chinese Opera*, which toured to virtually every town that had a theatre in the south of England. It was extraordinary the difference in reactions between one town and another. You'd go to one town which seemed to be a nice, gracious place, perhaps full of well-educated *Guardian* readers, and they wouldn't grasp the piece at all. And you'd go to another place which seemed like a bit of a dump, and have a great evening. So if I didn't know it before, I know it now, and I don't think I would dare to start predicting what an audience would like. And I also think, happily, most people have rather free reactions.

AF: As a young composer, did you ever receive the impression that composing music was a job for a boy?

JW: Firstly, at that time there were some very prominent composers that I knew of. Thea Musgrave was still living in this country and Elisabeth Lutyens was a very big figure. And I think Nicola LeFanu was having her first pieces performed. I went to a girls' school and I don't think it was ever suggested that there were things that girls weren't meant to do. Also it was the 1970s and very much the time of the women's movement. By 1975 we had an Equal Opportunities Act—not that it's done anyone any good—and it was an optimistic time. Maybe I could have rationalised some of the discouraging things that happened to me in that way, but it didn't occur to me. But then it's always a matter of surprise to me when one is discriminated against on grounds of gender—you think they can't possibly be doing this. I tend to be very trusting.

AF: The female colleagues I talk to are divided about whether to identify as a Female Composer and to embrace the idea of ghetto concerts of music by women. Some of them feel this is the only way to get a better deal; others think it's preferable to blend in with the crowd. What's your attitude?

JW: I find it so hard to hold rigorously to either of those things. My best hope for women composers is that we can find some kind of middle way—I think that's what women very often want to do. It's impossible not to be involved in women composers' concerts, just because they do happen—you can't exclude yourself from them. In the end, I think that if you want a career as a composer you do have to go with the existing structures and work your way through them. Partly because it seems to me that new music is so under-resourced that separate organisations for women are always going to be impoverished. I mean, I have ambitions as an opera composer. I just have to go with the English National Operas and the Covent Gardens, because I don't think I'm going to find the necessary level of support elsewhere. And I do think that the more women who work their way through existing male-dominated structures, the less male-dominated they will be. But I've been to women composers' concerts and made amazing discoveries, particularly of historical pieces—and realistically those pieces wouldn't appear otherwise, so I can see a use for them. But I agree with your use of the word 'ghetto', because, alas, the people you want to hear these composers aren't going to come to the concerts.

AF: Yes, it's a convenient way of avoiding a lot of music by women in a single evening.

JW: That's the point. It's also a wonderful method of clearing it out of the way and making it seem that the problem's been dealt with.

AF: But it's important not to underestimate the value to the composers themselves of hearing their work, whether or not it changes anything outside that particular concert.

JW: That's right and that's another reason I see both sides of it.

AF: The other area which I'm interested to ask you about is whether, as some of our colleagues have suggested, there is identifiably female music?

JW: My interest in music is in individual pieces. I'm not even really interested in individual composers—composers are always writing different sorts of pieces. So, for me, the generalisation becomes too wide. Also it's based on gender stereotypes which are in themselves too crude to be interesting.

AF: I feel awkward asking those questions, I must say, because it's not as if I ever ask male composers how it feels to be a boy.

JW: Well, I was going to say that over the years there is that feeling that we're always being asked about our identification with our gender. Now I feel quite assured about it, but in earlier years I felt under the microscope being asked those kinds of questions. But having said that, the questions still need to be asked from time to time. There is an imbalance and I think you have to keep an eye on the situation—it's not like it's going to be okay if you do nothing.

AF: What would you say that music is for?

JW: [*long pause*] Well, as you can see, I'm struck dumb by this question. In a way I can think of so many uses, but in the end, for me personally, it's just a mode of abstract thought that I enjoy. Listening to it or writing it: it's just the most fascinating thing. I think opera is one of the biggest occasions we have in modern western life, given the decline of religion; it's one of the very few places where everyone gathers with that sense of expectation of something big being played out. But I don't have a very good answer for you. I'm sure it's the same for every composer—once you really get into writing a piece, the issues of the music are so interesting that the idea of it having a use is beside the point.

London, July 1992

Franco Donatoni

A man without imagination

Franco Donatoni

At the top of the steep hill that leads to the Sydney residence of the Italian Consul-general to Australia there is an appropriately ambassadorial house. The front door is ajar and it opens into a lobby in 18th century style. There is no one about and no bell to ring, and it does not seem quite the thing to shout. I step outside again and look around. Across the garden sit two men, or rather two sets of legs in trousers—the top halves of their bodies are obscured by newspapers. After once more checking the lobby for a bell, I make my way over to the reading figures. It is a typical early spring afternoon for Sydney; the sun is glaringly bright, but the wind gusting off the harbour is fresh. At first the men in the garden chairs do not notice me, but eventually one of them looks up.

'I have an appointment with Franco Donatoni,' I tell him.

'I am the Consul-general,' he replies, rising and heading off in the direction of his tennis court, waving his arm to indicate the other newspaper, 'and this is Maestro Donatoni.'

The second newspaper is lowered, revealing a pudgy, grey-bearded face, with eyes for which the term 'beady' might have been coined. The composer leans his aldermanic figure towards me and shakes my hand. His smile displays a single tooth (bottom, right).

I had been told that the interview would be in English, but it is only now that I realise Donatoni's English is not the very best. My Italian consists of a handful of useful phrases for asking for things in restaurants. So our conversation is not an easy one. Where Donatoni's words appear here in quotation marks, only about half of them are actually his. The rest consists of my interpretation of his English, and of our brief attempt to communicate in French.

Franco Donatoni's life has been an unusual one. He was born in Verona in 1927, which puts him in the same generation as Nono, Berio, Boulez and Stockhausen. However, it is really only since the mid-1970s that he has taken his proper place amongst such celebrated company. The 20th century contains many examples of composers who discover their voices late. Elliott Carter and Michael Tippett, for example, were

116

both almost 40 years old before they began to write the distinctive sorts of music we now associate with them. In Donatoni's case, he was past 50. This is not to say there are no important works from earlier in his career, just that musical aesthetics and style, for this composer, have remained in a state of flux until comparatively recently: roughly once every seven years, Donatoni has stopped composing one sort of music and begun again with something else entirely.

Donatoni discusses this pattern in his life with the objectivity of a biographer. He refers to the various compositional styles and techniques he has embraced as 'periods'; the ends of those 'periods' and the consequent hiatuses are 'crises'.

'I've had many crises in my life,' he says, apparently resigned to having them. 'The last one was in 1984–85.'

Donatoni's initial impulse to compose came from his admiration for Bartók (an influence one would never pick in his recent music). In the 1950s, in common with most of the other European composers of his generation, he was drawn into the orbit of the contemporary music festival at Darmstadt in Germany. There he encountered Stockhausen, Boulez and the rest of the post-war avant-garde, and the effect of their influence was to turn him into a full-on serialist.

'Darmstadt was necessary for that post-war period, because it was there that Boulez, Stockhausen and Maderna created this new music. And also the public intolerance this aroused was important, just as it had been for Lenin during the Russian Revolution. Darmstadt was a big influence on me: my *Tre improvizationi*, performed at Darmstadt in 1958, was a bad copy of Boulez's second piano sonata. But it was a very stimulating time. I got to know Boulez and Stockhausen later, but at that time the big figure for me was Bruno Maderna. It was through him I discovered Boulez. Maderna and I were both in Verona and I used to see him almost every night. He was a very generous man.'

The next step for Donatoni was the diametric opposite of serialism. John Cage had made appearances at Darmstadt, but by the late 1950s his music was scarcely tolerated by the serialists there. Where Boulez and Stockhausen sought control over the music they composed, Cage had abdicated from the responsibility of making decisions about his work. Donatoni—whose susceptibility to strong influences by now seems to have been chameleon-like—followed Cage's example, and in the process came very close to ceasing composition completely.

'I was very influenced by chance operations in the scores of 1962–64. But 1965 was silence; I wrote nothing.'

Thirty years on, Donatoni's 'crisis' of 1965 seems, as he tells it, a mere anecdote—a minor snag in his development. But it was far more than this. Gerard Brophy, who studied with Donatoni in the early 1980s, relates an incident from that time which suggests the scale of this particular 'crisis'.

'It was in Venice,' Brophy recalls, 'in the cafe that's attached to the

Fenice theatre. Michael Smetanin and Ric Formosa were there too. And John Cage came up to me and said, "Hello. Is that Mr Donatoni over there? Could you introduce me, please?" So we went over, and I introduced them, and Donatoni was very pleasant to him—"Ah, si, si, maestro," and so on—and when Cage had gone Donatoni said: as "That bastard! He almost wrecked my life." '

The work which Donatoni composed to try to rid himself of Cage's influence was the chamber ensemble piece *Etwas ruhiger im Ausdruck*. Today it has almost become Donatoni's official opus 1 (the composer destroyed much of the music he had composed up to that point). *Etwas ruhiger . . .* won him his first real international attention; it is the earliest of his pieces to be regularly played today; it is also, in several ways, a precursor of the kind of music he now writes.

'In 1966, *Etwas ruhiger . . .* was another new beginning, where I returned to notating scores. I did this in order to "interiorise" the chance procedures, and I applied a kind of "automatism" to the mental processes—like a computer.'

The piece's German title (which roughly translates as 'Rather quieter in expression') is a cryptic instruction written over the eighth bar of the second of Schoenberg's piano pieces, opus 23. This bar became Donatoni's starting point for his own piece, which is a *pianissimo* whirlwind tour of the possible solutions to that musical phrase. Schoenberg's original gesture generates all the music in *Etwas ruhiger . . .* and ultimately turns up in its original form as Donatoni's final bar.

'I took that little fragment of Schoenberg and made it proliferate, like in Boulez's music. This involved many, many different techniques— from proliferation, through selection, cutting up the music, new selections, proliferation of those selections, and so on. This approach not only affects *Etwas ruhiger . . .*, but also *Souvenir* and all the works until 1974. And then, after that, there was a new crisis.'

The 1974 crisis was perhaps the most extended of them all. Not only did Donatoni stop composing again, he let it be known he had stopped. The reasons he gives for this suggest that he had failed to exorcise Cage's ghost completely.

'At this time my interest was really in mental processes and not in finishing scores. Because the score, for me, was just a commercial object to be handed over to the music industry. It was not mine.'

This time, Donatoni's musical silence lasted for nearly two years. Gerard Brophy explains the reasons for it and describes the period.

'He'd been interested in Cage, and he got to the point where he tried to exclude his ego from the music he was writing to such an extent that he thought, "Well, why write music at all?" And that was the crisis. He said he'd developed a cramp in his right hand and he couldn't hold a pen any more. So he became a proofreader of old manuscripts for the Milan music publisher Suvini Zerboni. He got rid of his studio (a lot of Italian composers have studios away from the family home—

that's where you write music and have your affairs). He bought this black bike and happily rode around Milan, going to Suvini Zerboni and doing his proofreading.

'Then he received a commission from Chigiana academy in Siena, and he turned it down. But his wife said, "Look, Franco, write this piece; you've given up composing—we all know that—but just one more piece won't hurt." So he was struck by this, and he wrote it, and that piece was *Ash*. I don't know whether he named the piece before he wrote it or after, but it was certainly like a phoenix rising from the ashes.'

Donatoni is convinced that his career moves in seven-year cycles, punctuated with 'crises'. Gerard Brophy maintains that this may once have been the case, but is no longer true, since Donatoni has been composing extremely fluently since 1977 (notwithstanding the composer's claim that he had another crisis as recently as 1984). But *Ash*, as Donatoni acknowledges, certainly marked the beginning of his current musical style; it was with *Ash* that he found his current, very distinctive voice.

'Yes, now it's very different, because after 1974—after that crisis—I became freer in the late 70s, with pieces like *Ash* and *Spiri* and *Arie*. Since the early 80s, and works such as *Tema*, *Cadeau* and *Le ruisseau sur l'escalier*, my music has become even more free. There has been a shift away from the earlier automatism; I invent more. Now my systems are "servants"—they are useful methods, but I decide the results. I am completely free to organise my music; to employ systems or not to employ systems. I might program one aspect of the music—for instance the durations of sections—and leave the others completely free. But I do not find it necessary to decide any of this in advance.

'In *Tema*, for example, there is no compositional scheme. The material comes from some pages of *L'ultima sera* for voice and five instruments, which I composed the year before *Tema*. It was a piece written during the period when I developed my intuitive approach and I was free to write what was in my mind. All my experience of automatism and so on was behind me at this moment—perhaps I was conscious of the result—but although I still write with some control there is no grand plan. I simply write . . . day after day.'

Donatoni's current and, perhaps, 'mature' voice is characterised by short, virtuosic pieces. Many of them are in two movements—more accurately, pairs of movements. Typically, his music has a glittering or shimmering quality in which fragments of musical material are juxtaposed, superimposed and then often suddenly assembled to form an epiphanous, melodic line. I suggested to the composer that in his recent music he had produced a new, utterly distinctive form of lyricism, but he was sceptical about this.

'I think that I am not a lyrical man. I have written for voice, for example in *Arie* and other pieces, but it is an instrumental approach to the voice—instrumental like in Bach.'

In Donatoni's music there is a very clear sense of the progression of ideas. Listeners can quite easily follow how a musical figure changes, develops, accrues new features and discards old ones. The obvious parallel to draw here is with the American minimalists of the 1970s, for whom the process was the piece.

'I am not interested in minimalism as such. There are perhaps a few works—not very important works, like *Estratto II* for example—where there is a minimal change in the material. One could link this to minimalism, but it isn't minimalism.

'I hope my music is very clear for listeners. For a long time I composed in panels, where there is one articulation of sound, then a break, then another articulation. Every musical moment is independent. For me this operation is no longer very satisfactory, because, in music like this, B comes after A, and C comes after B: this is a *chronology*, not a history, because there is no progress and the form is circular.'

Donatoni describes his new compositions as 'organic' in their musical growth from tiny fragments to fully worked out pieces. This is why *Etwas ruhiger . . .*, with its found Schoenbergian object, can be seen as premonitory for its composer.

'Now I always use a fragment given to me, or the fragment of another score. I need a fragment. Something that can then develop organically. And then I can go. I have no predetermined idea of the form. The form emerges. The *sense* of the form emerges.

'I never imagine music before I write it down. I have no imagination. I am a man without imagination. To imagine music without immediately *realising* that music is useless.

'Mental process is a very personal thing. It is very difficult to distinguish precisely between discovery and invention. Discoveries are given to you—you have to be open to them. When I am writing, I don't know whether I am inventing or discovering. The initial material is an invention, but after that the music suggests to me its own invention. And that is a problem. Is the musical material somehow active? Or do I have possession of this material? Because I am Franco Donatoni. Here I am. I can't put myself on the side of the material. I don't know if the material is active or not.

'For me, now, composing music is very physical. And it is important to try do it every day. I am an artisan—a craftsman—and I have to practise my craft. Of course, when I am travelling, like now, it is impossible to work every day. But when I am at home I work from very early—from five or six o'clock—until nine. Then I cook for myself—I am alone—and there is the telephone . . . But I will compose all day if I am allowed to. Inspiration comes when I put myself on the chair to write.'

It is probably just as well, given his former, highly suggestive disposition, that Donatoni no longer finds much inspiration in the work of other composers or even, he says, in other intellectual pursuits.

'I am not concerned with ideology or literature or pictures. For other composers this is important. For me inspiration is life. To be here in Australia, to be in Sydney, to be here with you . . . this will influence me. But I don't know how or when. My experience tells me that there is no immediate relationship between invention, intuition and rationality. Because intuition is on the right, and language is on the left. At the time of *Ronda*, for example, which I wrote in 1984, I was . . . not depressive . . . but almost depressive. And yet *Ronda* is a piece which is very exciting. There is no relationship between how I felt at the time and what I wrote.'

At the risk of provoking a new crisis (he is due for one, after all) I asked Donatoni which composers he holds in esteem today.

'From our century? Bartók—he was a great influence—and Goffredo Petrassi and Pierre Boulez; and my students too, because as a teacher if I am open to everyone, then it is possible to be influenced by my students. From other centuries: Mahler, Beethoven, Brahms—these are obvious names. But now I prefer the clear language of Mozart and Haydn . . . and Monteverdi.'

The sound of the Italian Consul-general's tennis game, which had formed a distant counterpoint to our conversation, has ceased. The wind has blown a few large grey clouds over the house, and I decide it is time to leave. I hazard one last question and ask Franco Donatoni if any works from his large recent output of music are particularly important to him.

'It is not possible. They are like my sons and it is not good to prefer one son to another.'

So I bid the composer farewell and begin my descent of the precipitous driveway. When I glance back across the garden, the Consul-general has returned, and the maestro and his diplomatic host have both disappeared once more behind their newspapers.

Sydney, September 1991

Sofia Gubaidulina

The hand of fate
Sofia Gubaidulina

Sofia Gubaidulina had been described to me by those who had met her as 'serene', 'warm', 'charming' and even 'saintly'—all of which is probably true, although, never knowingly having met a saint, I can only guess about the last.

Even five years ago, Gubaidulina was largely unknown outside her native country. Now, thanks to *perestroika*, her music is played and her name mispronounced in concert halls throughout the world. (It's G'bye-doo-l'na.) The composer, who is about to turn 60, is enjoying her success and the opportunities this provides for overseas travel.

Gubaidulina freely admits that, for a Soviet composer before Gorbachev, life was hardly easy. Composers had three options: to write State-commissioned (and State-approved) music; to appear to do so but (like Shostakovich) to lace it with irony; to do neither and court official neglect—or, worse, official attention. Gubaidulina chose this final option, or rather, as she herself might say, the option chose her.

What appears to radiate, both from the composer and her music, is a calm acceptance of things as they are; indeed, there is an unwillingness to become involved in the sordid politics of everyday life—Gubaidulina's work inhabits an altogether different plane. Like the music of many of her contemporary compatriots—Silvestrov and Schnittke and the Estonian Arvo Pärt—there is something seemingly spiritual about Gubaidulina's music. Pieces such as the violin concerto *Offertorium* (1980) and the austere *Seven Words* (1982) for solo cello, bayan (accordion) and string orchestra possess a quality which is plainly evident and yet impossible to define; one hears the spirituality but cannot pinpoint its musical source. Can the composer herself help?

'No,' she replies, 'I can't say in concrete terms what it is about my music which is spiritual. I would say that it is tied up with the music's general direction. In Russia and in Eastern Europe, I feel that spirituality is a very real musical direction. I don't know whether it is conscious or not, but it stems from a desire to connect heaven and earth.

'It is shared by a number of my colleagues such as György Kurtag,

124

Helmut Lachenmann and the late Luigi Nono, none of whom is a Soviet composer. I feel a deep spiritual affinity with these composers.'

I asked Gubaidulina about her childhood. When did she become a composer, and how? Her reply is straightforward: 'I can never remember not composing. From five years old, I started learning the piano, but I immediately wanted to do something for myself.'

Her early musical education brought disappointments. She sums up the restrictions she experienced in an image which must be familiar to many composers. The beloved grand piano of her childhood had what seemed to the young girl an enormous keyboard, but in her piano lessons she was restricted to a couple of octaves in the middle. The repertoire for an inexperienced pianist was typically banal, and Gubaidulina's instinct to improve these pieces, and generate for herself more interesting possibilities, was as strong as her desire to explore the outer reaches of the keyboard. On her arrival at college, restrictions of another sort came into play.

'The music of the European avant-garde was not unknown in Russia. Certainly, we were able to get records and scores, somehow or other. But the government in the 1940s and 50s didn't want students to know about western contemporary music; they even instigated searches in the colleges to see if students had some Stravinsky or Hindemith in their rooms.'

If such attitudes seem scarcely believable outside Stalin's Soviet Union, at least Gubaidulina never had to face the barriers of gender discrimination familiar to her western sisters.

'It was never a problem. The government was not interested in whether I was male or female. I certainly had a difficult time, but not because I was a woman. The difficulties were ideological ones. To stand as an individual artist and remain independent of all the ideological pressures that are placed on one, that is the great difficulty. I set myself the task to be totally free.'

Gubaidulina once supported herself by composing film scores. Today, her personal situation is very different. Her music is regularly performed in her own country and it is receiving more and more attention elsewhere. Recordings, too, are beginning to appear. For Gubaidulina herself, being in a foreign country and at a festival in which she is a featured composer are common occurrences. She says she hates to be a pessimist, but does not feel hopeful about the future of her country.

So, would she ever contemplate leaving for good?

'No, I don't want to leave. Fate deals you a certain hand; these are the cards you must play.'

Brisbane, August 1990

Alexander Goehr

A composer like Brahms

Alexander Goehr

I visited Alexander Goehr at his cottage in the village of Swaffham Prior, just outside Cambridge where he is Professor of Music. Following a very English tea of sandwiches and cherry cake, we talked in Goehr's study. Since this was his 60th anniversary year, it seemed appropriate to begin at the beginning.

AF: You come from a very specific musical background, in that your father Walter Goehr was both a conductor and a pupil of Schoenberg. When did you know that you were a composer?

AG: Obviously if you do come from that sort of background, being a composer of music is not so extraordinary as it would be from someone who came from a background with nothing in it. On the other hand there are some disadvantages in that. In my particular case, my father took a very negative view of my musical abilities when I was a child and I was rather ousted, so that I had the special complexity of a situation where on the one hand I knew all about it, and on the other hand I felt excluded from it. It was probably not till I was 15 or 16 that I really got interested in composition and it was like a guilty secret—I wouldn't have told my father and I postponed telling anybody until the last possible moment and then they reacted with horror.

AF: So while other teenage boys were busy secretly masturbating, you were secretly writing fugues?

AG: Yes. Well . . . not exclusively! But of course now that this is all long ago the strange thing seems to me to be how much one takes in without knowing it. I realise I know a lot of things which I never read. I know the contents of scores or books that I seem never to have studied—you know that phrase that it comes with the mother's milk—there are things I have feelings about that come from my background. Though there's a paradox here, because you're always trying to get away from that to do something new; but the more you try to get away, the more you're behaving archetypally.

128

AF: So at what stage did your father stop being disapproving of your music?

AG: When he died. He was very complex. He was himself a frustrated composer and he viewed conducting with considerable distaste and scorn; for him the real musical activity was composing. When I became a composer he took several attitudes at the same time. One was extremely constructive and helpful: he could, in a minute, give me a composition lesson which no one else ever gave me—he'd say, 'You do it like this actually . . . '—and he empathised with my ideas. But this also involved absolute demolition of a kind that no teacher would dare give a pupil—total demolition because it was very personal. He once performed a piece of mine—*The Deluge* [1957–58]—and it was a great success, and everyone asked him to do it again, and he was asked in many countries because it was quite a sensation, and he flatly refused— he never did it again. And then there were moments when he wanted to write pieces with me—to collaborate in some way—and he started getting out pieces he hadn't finished in 1932 and having another look at them. He died very young, and when he died I inherited his music and of course the first thing I was interested to know was whether it was just political circumstances—emigration and the need to earn a living—that had stopped him being a composer. And I think—I mean, God, he could compose well, but he wasn't a composer. He was a great light music composer and terrific at incidental music, but his longer structures were sort of derivative—there was something lacking. And he had been terribly annoyed with me, because he said, 'When I was 18, I earned my living at the operetta'—he was a natural, fluent musician, whereas I was impractical and oafish and writing twelve-tone works. And he said, 'This is bullshit! Why are you such a snob? Why do you sit without money, doing these bogus, highbrow works, when you could be earning a good living?' And I said, 'Look, I am not a snob—it's just that I'm not able to do these things that you can do.' But, of course, the greatest legacy of coming from that sort of a background was that it then became impossible for me to do what other composers of my generation did—to break out into totally new things. I seem always to be travelling the opposite way, because the sneering faces of those Schoenbergians and my father are not entirely construc- tive: saying, 'Yes, of course it's dead easy for you; you go off to Cologne and follow Stockhausen; untalented people like you can do that with the greatest of ease and write electronic music and that'll be just marvellous.' And so it had the effect that the one thing I really cared about was to prove to this now long-dead individual that, in the sense that Brahms was a composer, I could be one too. To this day I can allow myself no special privileges: I can't say, 'I'm a modern composer, and you don't understand my work'; I regard it as a personal defeat if people can't follow my pieces—which is generally the case, obviously.

AF: How did you end up in Manchester? A lot of stuff has been written about the Manchester school—but why Manchester?

AG: Well—like most things in my life—for no pertinent reason. I was a conscientious objector. I was very politically left and, having been in the Young Communists, I then joined the Socialist Zionist Association, which I came upon in London by chance. It was a sort of kibbutz movement. And they sent me to Manchester as a political activist to teach Marxism—it was a case of the land of the blind, where the one-eyed man is king; I really knew very little about it. So I was a political organiser. My father knew Iso Elinson, a pianist at the Manchester College, and he wrote him a card and Elinson recommended me to Richard Hall for composition lessons. When National Service was over, the Socialist Zionists wanted me to become an agricultural worker in Israel, which I wasn't frightfully keen to become. So my scholarship to study classics at Oxford was transferred and I stayed in Manchester, which, at that time, was a nonsensical thing to do because no one—certainly no one in the south—took Manchester seriously.

AF: So was it a fluke that the particular bunch of people who became the Manchester group all turned up there at the same time?

AG: Yes. The thing that was not a fluke was that we became a group. I mean Max[well Davies] and Harry [Birtwistle] and Gary [Elgar] Howarth and John Ogdon might well have all been there anyway—I certainly didn't bring them there—but that we became a group was surely my doing. It was partly old Communist Party stuff: the idea of making a cell, transposed onto a different set of circumstances, with ideology and party lines and all the rest of it. I was playing a slightly adolescent game. Also they didn't come from musical backgrounds— they were, in a sense, provincial—and although they were gifted and talented they wouldn't necessarily have known so quickly that they could be what they later became. No one in Manchester in the 1950s would have known that you could become a professional composer; they'd have said, 'Don't be silly, get a proper job'. Max went and became a school teacher, because it was the right thing to do.

AF: I think every composer, at some stage, needs someone else to say, 'Yes, you can do this'.

AG: Yes, exactly. There'd been no composers from the Royal Manchester College, except Rawsthorne some time earlier.

AF: After Manchester you went to Paris and studied with Messiaen. Can you say what he gave you?

AG: At the time, paradoxically, the main influence that Messiaen had on me had already taken place before I went to Paris. It was from the scores and the excitement of the performance of *Turangalîla*. So, in fact, when I got to Paris I was largely disappointed. This was where Boulez was, this was where Stockhausen had been, and I thought it was going to be an eye-opener. Well, in the short run, it wasn't. The classes, in one sense, were deeply disappointing and about things that didn't interest me. On the other hand they had the effect of taking several inches off me; I had a sort of crisis of confidence. In Manchester we'd been playing a game—we had this fantasy that we were great masters—and so coming up against Messiaen you suddenly realised that you were a noisy little boy who didn't know anything. So I felt I had to start again. I was probably too young and arrogant to appreciate what Messiaen had to offer, and yet the classes were entirely memorable—I can remember almost everything he said, 35 years later, and over the years, while I still don't find any of his ideas satisfactory, all of them present ways of doing things. In my case, first of all, the modal construct harmony—which I never used, because it always sounds like Messiaen if you do—led to my employing a kind of modal serialism for a time. More recently, his attitude towards duration has become quite important to me—the idea of composing in absolute real time structures. I think Messiaen got it wrong theoretically, but I think he was on to something about the absolute durations which things have as opposed to bar structures which exist in the Schoenbergian world. The third thing that I gained from Messiaen is to do with Debussy. To my mind, nobody has satisfactorily understood the relationship between harmony and form in Debussy. I don't think Messiaen quite understood it either, but he gave me the material with which one could go further and understand it. The influence of Debussy on me in the last ten years has been through seeing something which is not what Messiaen saw, but is via what Messiaen saw.

AF: Can we take a hypothetical situation? You have a very talented student, but—it being 1992—the student really doesn't know what sort of music to compose . . .

AG: Then he's not talented. There's a connection between compositional talent and imagination. I've never met anyone talented who didn't have some notion of what he wanted to compose—however stupid from my point of view. The question then is what attitude do you take? You know Nono gave a lesson to Robin Holloway—believe it or not, this took place. Nono immediately says, 'What you're doing is complete bullshit! This is totally valueless and of absolutely no interest and stop it.' Now that's one way, and all the Darmstadt didacticism operated in that way—Boulez would say, 'Ça, c'est du merde!—take it away and bring me something else'. I would never say that to a student. My job, in so far as I function as a teacher, is to try to make students more themselves, not less themselves. I can say to somebody, 'Look, I'm terribly sorry, I'm not your man.' After all, to be someone's teacher is a form of service. They pay for goods rendered, and if you can't deliver the goods you have to say so. Teaching composition is not a form of political activity; you're not trying to convert people. Some people want their hand holding: I've had close relationships with students and we could almost have written each other's pieces. At other times the best you can do is to give some advice about what pencil to use—some people don't want much. Some students want to do all the talking and they need to—I was one such. I didn't care what a teacher said, I wanted to tell him; and, by telling him, I learned.

AF: A few years ago you spoke of your desire to return to a common musical language—I think you even went so far as to suggest that what Boulez was doing in his Paris bunker—trying to invent the language of the future—was 'looking pretty stupid', specifically in the light of the images one sees on the nightly news of people starving to death in third world countries.

AG: Of course. First of all I'm afraid composers can't do much to help starving people. In 1991, when all the ideologies collapsed, it was a very difficult thing for someone like me—who believed in those ideologies—to come to terms with. This doesn't particularly mean that I've changed my views about anything, but it's difficult to live with. Because a line which started with my coming of age ended then. In a way, there was a link between my post-war political ideology—which had to do with the reorganisation of society—and (crazy as it may seem) Boulez and the idea of constituting a new musical language in which all the elements were purged of their old associations. Even if I was a poor follower of those views, I believed that. But there comes a point where one has to say that the idea of a new musical language is a self-indulgent fantasy of the very rich and doesn't concern anybody in the real world. Yet, those people in the real world are not to be scorned as certain aspects of modernism did by a kind of hooliganism. It's not to be assumed that because a country is backward, its people have no musical aspiration; they have great aspiration, and it seems to me that one ought to stand in relation to them as a pupil and not as a missionary—they are a traditional culture. Now perhaps the reason that we are in musical difficulties is precisely because the values of our traditional cultures have disintegrated. When I talked about common material I chose my words carefully. I didn't want to say 'natural' material and get hoisted on that Hindemithian bandwagon, and it wasn't a tonal movement that concerned me. I felt that artificially constructed music had an expressive limitation; that Boulez and Harry, who *construct*, do very good things, but the ceiling is there. To remove that ceiling you've got to get away from artificial systems, you've got to find a way of . . . I'm afraid I have to say a way of returning. I don't want music to be archaic, although some of mine on the way was deliberately so—I was limiting myself—but I really was concerned to try and regain some sort of freedom . . .

AF: Are you talking about returning to older techniques or forms?

AG: No, not necessarily at all. In my worry about this I've sometimes gone perilously near neo-classical forms. I'm never interested in style as such, but there's been a reason why I've taken up . . .

AF: Fugues, chaconnes . . .

AG: Fugues, chaconnes, sonatas—yes. And then again that ultimately isn't what concerns me. I wrote down the other day in connection with Kafka that, in a sense, when you compose, all the material exists already in the world. There's nothing you can invent, but you can either synthesise the thing into some new form or fix it in a duration. The problem of the aspiration to compose meaningfully or well or transcendentally or whatever is that you fix your material in an absolute duration so that it occupies it all. Most of the time we only fix a bit of it and the rest is redundant and repetitive. In order to fix you can use old techniques. I mean, first of all, a composer has the right to use any technique he chooses—if he wants to shit on the canvas, he can shit on the canvas. The only measure we have of viability is whether the end result produces something new—and here there's no talk of returning: you have to do something new. But *how* you do something new is a different thing; you can use all techniques.

AF: But just as, say, architecture in this century has altered—I mean its appearance has altered, the design has altered *alongside* the use of new materials—steel, concrete, whatever—is it not possible that new musical technology can produce a new musical vocabulary, a new language?

AG: I think there's a confusion here between material and mental acts. If you say to me that there are new sounds, because we've found new ways of orchestrating—yes. If you say that electronic equipment throws up new material and new manners in which they behave—yes, sure. There must be millions of potential new sound materials available all the time. But I believe Boulez—although he aspires to a Bauhaus point of view, of developing according to the nature of the material—deludes himself. The serial-derived methodology which he employs is a way of imposing an order on new material. But that doesn't lead to new music; new music out of new material is where the material is allowed to make its own forms. Carrying your architectural analogy further, if it doesn't produce anything useful—in which anyone can live and function—it's not much good. But one reason why I haven't been involved in new musical materials is because I haven't got a good enough ear. I can just about manage the aural network of relationships that exist in conventional music, but I'm not gifted enough aurally to have become an exploratory composer in the sense that Stockhausen is one. Stockhausen really has achieved things with new sounds because of aural imagination; I don't think my imagination is aural, I think it's intellectual. Regrettably—but, you know, that's all I can do.

AF: Well, that brings us very neatly to those composers who have no interest in intellectual music—who, indeed, eschew the idea of music that makes demands on its listeners. John Tavener, for instance, told me the other day that this is precisely his aim.

AG: I suppose I would describe this as a super-intellectual point of view. In so far as there is a reaction to an arid intellectualism which preceded it in the 1950s and 60s, I'm sympathetic to it. I do think that a lot of music of that era conveniently ignored all sorts of things; you lined up behind the flag and it didn't matter whether it sounded nice, or whether anyone was interested in it, or whether it was playable. Yet, today, when it's fashionable to scorn these things, one should also defend the very considerable achievements of that time. I think these people—the Taveners, the Pärts and so on—their hiding behind religiosity has many antecedents: it's a bit like the pre-Raphaelites. I simply am not in favour of a bogus, theocratic culture and its cultural appurtenances; it strikes me as absurd. Like all movements of fashion, it exceeds what it can provide. If what Tavener, Pärt and Górecki claim to be able to provide they could provide, then well and good; from the little that I've heard they fall so far short. But there's a certain freshness about it if you've been buggering about with seven in the time of five, and nine in the time of eight, and pitch levels that make no sense and it sounds hideous, and then someone comes along and says you don't have to listen to all this garbage, what you need is to have a nice bath in my pot of golden syrup and you'll feel absolutely lovely. But to me Tavener sounds like someone carrying a little poster saying 'I am wholemeal bread. I am sincere. I am simple. I cut away the intellectual complications of life. Look at me!'. That seems to me a posture, because the world is immensely complicated and in deep despair, and Tavener and Pärt seem like a lot of pseudo-prophets and poor ones at that. And anyway the music is intolerable to listen to because it's just so bloody boring!

AF: You've mentioned pseudo-prophets—let's talk about a real prophet and your new piece *The Death of Moses*. You spoke about religiosity and bogus spirituality, but to what extent are you aiming at something spiritual in your own music? Are you a religious composer?

AG: Now you touch me on a very tricky issue. George Steiner was sitting in the garden here and accused me of being a religious composer. And I guffawed loudly. And he said, 'Well what's the name of your next piece?' And I said, 'Well actually it's called *The Death of Moses*.'

And he said, 'There you are! And before that it was the Anabaptists,[1] and that's what I mean.' I find this a very complex issue. First of all, I'm not aiming at anything except trying to write music.

AF: But Sandy, if you call the piece *The Death of Moses* . . .

AG: I called it *The Death of Moses* because I'm setting poems which have that title.

AF: So the music and the words are not related?

AG: No, they're very closely related. Why did I pick those poems? I don't know. I picked them because certain words have resonances for me and often—I have to admit—they are religious words. Yet I don't consider myself a religious person in the sense of being a believer. I think this tendency to write works with religious texts has to do with the residue of socialist ideas, because a lot of socialist ideology was Judeo–Christian in its origins. Right up to Shelley, people with anarchist–socialist views borrowed religious symbolism from psalms and so forth, because these words to some extent had egalitarian or apocalyptic implications. Now, you can't find words which directly say these things in a modern tongue, because there aren't any. Okay, you read Neruda and other left-wing poets and sometimes you find some words you could use, but basically, when you're dealing with this territory which concerns me, you're dealing not with individual things but with collective things. I remember sitting in Edinburgh listening to Giulini rehearsing Beethoven's *Missa Solemnis*, and feeling an enormous urge to set the Communist Manifesto for large chorus and orchestra—'Workers of the world unite, you have nothing to lose but your chains' is just as good as anything that happens in the *Missa Solemnis*. Why couldn't I do it? Why are we smiling even at the thought? Because it's too topical, it's too actual. Now *The Death of Moses* is a good example of what I'm talking about. I was in Jerusalem and a friend of mine, who'd momentarily become head of the radio there, had some money at his disposal to commission a Holocaust commemoration piece. And he asked me if I'd like to write it. 'No,' I said, without any hesitation, 'I most certainly would not—not for any sum of money.' Because what do you do? It's impossible. That night, my wife Amira and I sat together with an old friend of hers, a very good poet called Carmi, and I said, 'Look, I feel bad about this. It's absolutely clear to me that one mustn't touch such things. On the other hand, we're meant to be artists in the modern world, and we ought to be able to deal somehow with the big issues—it's no good just setting little sonnets by Mallarmé.' So we discussed this, and Carmi said, 'Well, in my opinion, there are only two ways to deal with the Holocaust: one is the Abraham and Isaac story; the other one

---

1   The opera *Behold the Sun* (1984).

is "The Death of Moses".' Now Abraham and Isaac is too close to Christianity. 'The Death of Moses', which I didn't know, is unique, because it's folk poetry; it's nothing like the Moses of the Bible. This is an old man whose time has come to die and who simply doesn't want to. He objects; he says, 'I don't want to die, and there's no reason why I should.' Carmi said, 'There you have a symbol; there you've got the concentration camps.' The important thing about the Holocaust is that the people refused to die. That's the only message of any pride that one can draw. So you see you've got medieval poetry, but the words are not being used for a bogus Jewish or Christian purpose, they're being used because they have a resonance—if only for me—such that I can compose. I chose to do this piece this year—I'm half the age that Moses was when he had to go—and the refusal to give up, that's a positive thing. And that's why I liked those words: it's got nothing to do with Moses or God or anybody else.

AF: Since this is an anniversary year for you, let's look back at your early pieces: the *Little Symphony* [1963], *Pastorals* [1965], the *Symphony in One Movement* [1970], the music–theatre triptych [1968–70]. When you hear those pieces how do you feel about them?

AG: You know, as far as I'm concerned, all my pieces should be played all the time. Obviously there are certain constraints on the possibility of this, not least the presence of other composers in the world. I've never been much concerned with my own work: once it's done, once I've heard it, I generally lose interest. They're erring children, and maybe they stay alive and maybe they die. I've never been a very fashionable composer—at least, not for a long time—or anybody's darling. But the one thing that gives me great comfort is that a lot of my old works don't die, they do come up again, and when I've heard them I haven't often felt that they fall to pieces in the way that a lot of people's old pieces do. You try listening to a Penderecki piece written in 1960. It's a very salutary experience—there's nothing there. In the recurrences of my old pieces I'm only interested to know whether they're an embarrassment or not. And I've been, on the whole, comforted.

AF: Have you ever axed pieces from your catalogue?

AG: No. They axe themselves. My father used to say that what is not necessary in this world disappears by itself.

Cambridge, July 1992

Karlheinz Stockhausen

Constellations

Karlheinz Stockhausen

The man in the uniform behind the reception desk of Birmingham's Grand Hotel had told me that Mr Stockhausen was called away unexpectedly, but that he would be back within the hour and had expressed the hope that I would wait. I sit in the bar and ponder the meeting.

Stockhausen is a significant point of reference for music in the second half of the 20th century. In the first place, in the early 1950s he was one of the principal exponents of strict musical organisation. Later he moved towards musical forms which permitted far greater intuition, arriving ultimately in the late 1960s at pieces whose 'scores' amounted to little more than poems that served as springboards for group improvisation. Since then the composer has changed many more times. He regards each piece as a new beginning and style as an almost irrelevant concern.

In the 1970s he began an operatic project called *Licht* (Light) which will occupy him well into the 21st century and will consist, finally, of a cycle of seven large-scale theatrical works, each named for a day of the week. Such ambitious thinking is by no means a recent development in Stockhausen's work, however. It is hard to think of any other living composer who has produced so many major works: virtually each piece of Stockhausen is a unique event, with its own personality, its own frame of reference—even, and quite consciously, its own ensemble.

The door to the bar suddenly swings open and the bulky figure of Stockhausen himself is there, looking about him in a rather agitated manner. I give him a wave and he rushes over, expressing great concern that I have had to wait.

We adjourn to a rather public hotel alcove, together with Suzanne Stephens and Kathinka Pasveer (the composer's in-family clarinet and flute players, whom he introduces merely as 'my colleagues'). As we talk, a Tibetan Buddhist monk in a saffron robe appears by the composer's left shoulder. For a moment I wonder whether he is also part of Stockhausen's entourage, but, when he finally notices him, the composer gives a little start of surprise and then simply continues talking, as though this sort of thing happens to him all the time.

I wanted to ask Stockhausen first about the nature of his musical statements. Why are there practically no minor works in his catalogue? Why is everything conceived on such an ambitious scale?

'I have had very few possibilities in my life to compose for specific commissions, and when I was asked to write a piece for a special occasion, I always tried to compose what *I* had to do next, and to convince the person or the society who commissioned the new work that this is what I wanted to do. I seem to have a permanent flux of projects, and each is somehow the result of the previous one, but it is also the result of an inner vision.

'For example, we are here in Birmingham and I have been participating for three days in rehearsals for *Sternklang*. This is music for a park, composed in 1971–72. But *Sternklang* is in a chain of spacial compositions which I started in 1953.'

Sternklang is typical of its composer's work in the sense that it is an event. The work requires not only a park, but also a moonlit summer's night. Hidden in the bushes are five groups of performers on podia. The groups call to each other with musical signals, the audience is free to move around.

'That is one aspect of the piece—the aspect for the human child— but the other aspect is far more intriguing for me, as a composer of sound and the movement of sound: how I synchronise each group within itself, and every now and then synchronise all five groups—even though the whole oval layout of the five groups takes four or five hundred yards. Every now and then I send so-called "sound runners" from one group to another, carrying a "sound model" which is a period of music with a specific melody and rhythm and sequence of timbres, also with text using the names of star constellations. These runners run from their own group to another or several other groups and carry their model, singing it, or playing it with a portable instrument, and the other group imitates this runner and picks up the sound model and continues transforming it.'

In spite of the unique nature of Stockhausen's park music, there are numerous connections between *Sternklang* and some of the composer's other works. For example, the way in which performers can influence each other, sending out musical call signs which are picked up and imitated, transforming one another's material, interrupting at will: these features recur in other Stockhausen works. Also, like a good deal of the composer's music, *Sternklang* lasts a full evening.

'I have been trying to expand the duration of a given composition— *Sternklang* lasts two and a half to three hours. Before that I tried to compose works of a comparable length, but not as long as *Sternklang*: *Hymnen* [1966–67] is more than two hours, *Mantra* [1970] is 72 minutes, *Momente* [1962–69] is about two hours. I'm always worried if it will work, that you can listen to a two-and-a-half hour musical process without losing interest—it needs a lot of participation on behalf of the musicians to invent—not on the spot, but during long rehearsals.'

Quite so. But where are these players? In our orchestras? In our music colleges?

'You are faced with the problem of finding musicians who are not working under normal conditions with a conductor, in an orchestra with fixed hours and repertoire studied in a conservatory. For example, one of the five groups here in Birmingham consists of players from the symphony orchestra. They are good musicians, but the moment they are faced with this guided improvisation they are lost; they cannot really play synchronously, so one of them is constantly beating time which is terribly disturbing, because the music is not really periodic. It needs a different attitude altogether to shape music which needs personal decisions in favour of the other players. It will take a long, long time before *Sternklang* is taught in conservatories.'

Inevitably Stockhausen's music has frequently been performed under less than ideal conditions, particularly when the composer himself has not been on hand to guide the rehearsal period. Other works, because of their difficulty, have made only rare appearances in the concert hall. I wondered about the composer's apparently stoical attitude.

'I am generally freer in my spiritual goal. I have never been depressed when a work wasn't played for 20 or 30 years; it would have been nicer if it had been played, but it doesn't depress me. I go on as long as I live, because I think the lifespan is extraordinarily short and I have so many projects—many of them described in sketches—which I will never be able to realise, because there will not be time. Maybe a future generation will see all these seeds and will use the inventions and discoveries and formations that I have written.'

Stockhausen's opinion of his own importance in musical history—accurate or not, and I suspect it probably is—could never be called modest. The composer's belief in himself has also been necessary for the sheer volume of music he has produced. When one considers, also, that he in a sense reinvents his music and himself from piece to piece, that workload becomes almost unthinkably great. But how can he really start each new project *tabula rasa*? Surely there must be a continuation of thought from one work to the next?

'Yes and no. For example, for the last two years I have been heavily involved in an electronic music studio, developing what I call "octophony". There is a cube of loudspeakers; each corner of the cube has two speakers, which makes sixteen speakers. I have experimented in the studio with an electronic work which is now called *Octophony*—it's part of the second act of *Tuesday* from *Licht*.

'Together with this electronic music I have composed instrumental music for "sound invaders": two groups of musicians—mainly brass players, but also people with portable synthesisers and invented new percussion instruments. The players carry loudspeakers on their bodies and, through gangways, they invade the auditorium where the audience is sitting.

'*Octophony* is related to *Gesang der Jünglinge* [1955–56] for four loudspeakers, to *Kontakte* [1959–60] for four loudspeakers, to *Gruppen* [1955–57] for three orchestras surrounding the public in a semi-circle, and to *Carré* [1959–60] for four choirs and four orchestras at the four cardinal points. So it goes on from piece to piece, this exploration of space composition, but with *Octophony* I had no idea whether the vertical sound movements would work. So it's true that I have experience that I can use; at the same time I have no experience of certain aspects that I'm trying for the first time.'

Stockhausen's teacher was Olivier Messiaen, whose death a few weeks before this conversation prompted me to ask Stockhausen about the French composer.

'Two days ago I talked with my friends about the death of Messiaen. I went to Paris in 1952 because I was deeply touched by his *Trois petits liturgies* which I had heard as a student in Cologne. Later I heard at Darmstadt his *Quatre études de rythme* for piano. There was an atmosphere in Messiaen which struck me as being new and yet very lyrical, very poetic. When I was in his class I was very disappointed because there was nothing of the atmosphere.

'And now he's dead. Since that time when I studied in his class I haven't followed his work, because when I heard it occasionally I was even more disappointed because it did not develop enough for me and the harmonies were too similar to the harmonies and constellations of chords that I have experienced in other music.

'When I listen to the work of another composer, I am always looking not only for a talent for combining things, but also for something one has never heard before: details of chordal constructions, tonal constructions, rhythmic constructions, microtonal constructions, microrhythmic constructions which open up a world in the same way that biologists and astronomers discover new worlds. Messiaen didn't do that for me. I had the highest respect for him and, when I think of him now, I say he was my master for a certain time. But my relation to the past is extremely limited now. Nobody can teach me something.'

The particular *étude* of Messiaen that made such a strong impression on Stockhausen was entitled *Mode de valeurs et d'intensités*. In this piece Messiaen subjected his musical material—consisting of single pitches—to the most rigorous of formal procedures in which the lengths of each individual sound and the intensity of its articulation are the result of serial procedures. The piece's influence on Stockhausen can be detected almost immediately in the piano part of *Kreuzspiel*, composed in 1951, the year after Stockhausen heard the piece. I suggested to him that it was the sound world of the Messiaen piece, rather than its compositional technique, that made the greater impact.

'Yes. Definitely. Definitely. Afterwards I improvised myself on the piano to create a similar atmosphere of these dots in the air; it had this association, for me, of looking at the sky, where the dots create a music of isolated sounds which touch our soul—like when we look at a star constellation in the night sky and that gives us the feeling that we are cosmic beings. These isolated notes make one long for another kind of world.'

The ramifications of such thinking had a far greater effect, it would appear, than merely influencing the composer's piano writing. Twenty years later Stockhausen was still fascinated with stellar imagery, and not only in *Sternklang*. I told him that it was hearing a performance of his work *Ylem* (1972) that had made me want to write music.

' "Ylem" means "explosion"; it is the universal big bang. It associates the concept of a big bang where the universe explodes every 83 billion years. In between it expands for about half the time, then contracts. The universe *breathes* from one big bang to the next.'

The piece begins with an explosion in the form of a tam-tam stroke. The players, who are for the most part grouped around an open grand piano, heads bowed, suddenly jerk into life, playing the notes of the tritone A–E flat loud and fast. As the piece proceeds, these players move away from the piano into the auditorium and the sounds they produce become less regular, the pitches, registers and dynamics more diverse. By the middle of *Ylem* the musical universe has expanded. Each player individually makes one 90-second pause, shouts the syllable 'Hu!' (the name of God) and the entire piece goes into reverse as the universe contracts once again. Given that this process normally takes 83 billion years, *Ylem* might well have turned out to be Stockhausen's longest piece to date. In fact it lasts a mere 25 minutes.

Perhaps the most difficult aspect of the work for its performers, however, is the fact that, with the exception of the opening tritone, no other pitches are specified. Neither are there rhythms—nor, indeed, any musical notation at all. The players must set up what Stockhausen has called 'telepathic' communications with each other, and this, as one might expect, leads inevitably to further rehearsal difficulties.

'I will do *Ylem* again this year with the Ensemble Modern in Frankfurt. I'm sure that they cannot play *Ylem* easily, because most of the players are afraid that they might play rubbish. Rehearsals are painful for musicians who are used only to conductors or to playing from scores. Nevertheless I think it important to shape sounds judged only by the ear, with a guiding score but not with a deterministic prescription.'

Ylem can certainly be a painful rehearsal process for musicians. Having arranged performances of it myself, I know, at first hand, the results of pulling the musical rug out from under players who are used to the normal quota of 'deterministic prescription'. Their responses have ranged from tears to abuse.

The other score of Stockhausen's which had a strong impact on me is the vocal sextet *Stimmung* (1968). A series of performances which I directed and sang in with five of my students required months of rehearsal to come to terms with the composer's 'guiding score', not to mention the harmonic singing required of its performers—the production of overtones by means of altering vowel sounds and focusing the voice at the front of the head. I told the composer about my experience and asked him to describe the circumstances surrounding the first rehearsals for the work.

'For the first performance in 1968 I worked for almost a full year, twice a week with good singers. They had worked together with Mr Deller in Cologne singing pre-baroque music, so they had already very instrumental voices. Nevertheless, they sang in the throat and it took quite a long time for them to sing mainly in the skull—to make the skull resonate. The microphone technique itself took a long time before they learned how to pronounce consonants without producing pops and cracks, and how to support the overtones with special positions of the microphone. The ritual of sitting together on the floor, cross-legged, took quite a while for European singers—they were not used to that. At the time when it was first performed in Paris they wrote that it was a "hippy camp". But I liked that comment.

'I think we achieved some very good examples in particular through the 1970 performances at the World Fair in Japan where we performed it with the same ensemble every second or third day for 183 days. We came to a certain smoothness and flexibility that the piece needs, and yet we had to insist that the right spiritual mood was achieved before each performance. Because it is a sacred work: one has to call the names of the divinities of many different religious traditions of this planet in a fashion that the listeners can believe. In many of my works you need a performer who is religious—deeply religious—not in the orthodox way, but [so] that the musicians have an aura which makes the listeners feel that making music is a sacred act and that the sounds have a spiritual force. The sounds must be clean and the performers' souls must be clean when they make the sounds. This is not true of all my works—it's not true of my orchestral works, because I know that the orchestral players cannot be prepared in such a fashion.'

Another feature of *Stimmung* is the incorporation of frankly erotic poems by the composer, which are intoned in German at various points in the piece.

'They create, in this spiritual atmosphere, a sensuality in the way they are spoken; also, for those who understand German, there is sensuality in the content of the words. Also in the performances that I made the singers are very beautiful singers, it is important that the three girls and the three men are very handsome and have very good bodies and radiate youth and freshness and very positive spiritual vibrations.'

At this point I began to doubt that my performance of the work had been as authentic as I had hoped, and hastily assured the composer that at least five of the six singers—my students—had been young and fresh, even if the bass had let the side down a bit. Stockhausen laughed momentarily, before becoming suddenly serious and fixing me with a stare.

'Not necessarily. No, no. The opposite! One needs people of warm character for performing *Stimmung*, not mechanics!' I could see how it was possible to fall under this man's spell.

If a great many of Stockhausen's more recent pieces—from the 1960s on—require performers who are able to participate in the music to the point of shaping and controlling aspects of the piece normally stipulated in the score, his early works were far more traditionally rigid in their requirements. Not only this, but Stockhausen's composing methods were more rigid then. I asked what had occurred to bring about the composer's freer approach to composition.

'When I was a student in the Cologne conservatory I had to learn to write musical compositions in given styles, to make Buxtehude chorale preludes or a fugue in the fashion of Johann Sebastian Bach or Böhm; sonatas; *Lied* forms. When I made my exam I had to write a chorale improvisation for organ in four hours and the exposition of a sonata, and if I wanted to make a good exam I had to obey the rules rather than letting myself be free and doing something that the teacher would not accept.

'Then I went to Paris and in order to be accepted into the conservatory there one had to go through another exam. I fell completely through because although I had been number one in fugue writing at the Cologne conservatory a couple of months before, I didn't know the French way of fugue writing. There was a girl sitting next to me and I showed her what I had done, because I was very worried, and she said, "Impossible!". What I am trying to say is that rules of composition put me in a situation where I was cerebrally completely taken by this difficult task.'

If the musical climate after the second world war no longer favoured traditional methods of teaching, it by no means encouraged freedom. In the early 1950s Stockhausen's interest in post-Webern integral serialism led him to draw up his own sets of rules for composition and these, in turn, created new difficulties.

'For the first piano pieces I had made such strict rules for myself that I couldn't find the next note sometimes for hours, sometimes for days! At the end of the eighth piano piece, which is so simple and so short, the last bar I couldn't find for days because I told myself you cannot change the octave if there has not been a major seventh or a minor ninth between the given note and the next octave but one. I had jumped from octave one to octave three to octave five to octave seven—now how do I jump to octave four? I have to write a minor second, but I have to hide it away, you see, because I don't want minor seconds. Etcetera. So I found myself in a situation where I couldn't find the last note.'

By the time he began to compose *Gruppen* in 1955, Stockhausen's music had reached a point where its reliance on what he refers to as 'statistical rhythms' meant that the composer felt alienated from his own musical inventions.

'I could never hum or beat a rhythm of my own piece. So I said this cannot go on; what comes comes. I would lie down in my working room and imagine anything—all of a sudden the tuba would go wild. And I said to myself you can't do that. And then another voice said why not? So I made sketches and let the tuba run wild, and the piano have all of a sudden a cadenza, and the E flat clarinet the same.

'So I broke open my own construction. And I was terribly ashamed, like a Catholic who has sinned terrifically! But all my pieces then became more or less broken by sins against my own rules and laws. And that is what I call intuition: the flashes of instantly heard events which you cannot fit into your system, because the system is not wide enough. This is where I learned that if I want to be truthful to myself then I have to allow these intuitive moments.

'I had to learn how I could prepare a system for a given composition which is original enough not to allow in references to my other works (not to speak of cliches of other composers or of the past) and yet would be open to the daily sound events which I hear when I sleep, when I walk, when I drive in a car. I hear these things and note them. I carry with me certain events for years and don't know where I can get rid of them in a given composition. And yet some day I will get rid of them because they are so fascinating.

'The fascination of sound visions; the fascination of being a very good engineer: these two things are the permanent problem of modern composition. There are younger composers—my students—who only react to associative composition. They sit down and what comes comes, and they hear a lot of other music. Several of my students, who have become very well known now, they listen to my music while they are composing, or they watch television while they compose in order to get enough stimuli. Some kind of mixture comes out of this. There are certain chameleons amongst present-day composers—they call themselves post-modernists—and they mix everything they can steal, and paint the stolen elements with different colours so that you cannot identify them immediately. They are enormous garbage containers of pre-existing sound figures and cliches and out of this source comes something else. There is no unifying spirit. It's the opposite: the will *not* to have a unifying spirit, to have everything and to combine everything in an unusual fashion. I think that is a big mistake.'

Stockhausen's own music is by no means free from quotation. Especially in his electronic pieces, from *Gesang der Jünglinge* on, there are frequent references to other existing music, generally in the form of recordings integrated into the musical whole. In *Hymnen* the national anthems of many different countries provide a particularly strong series of reference points. So I asked Stockhausen how he justified this very pluralistic approach to composition whilst insisting that he was no post-modernist.

'The basic problem of combining intuition and pre-planning is the most urgent question of the second half of the 20th century. More urgent than at any time before. Even in the first half of the century it was easier to compose: for certain composers and painters, if you say, "I go abstract", then you go abstract and that's it. This means that nothing that the world has heard before will enter my piece otherwise it will destroy it. This was the first ten years of my life as a composer as well.

'But in *Gesang der Jünglinge* already I had to face words which have associations—snow, ice, winter, wind, moon—and you hear certain sound events in that piece which I cannot justify with my construction; they are associative events. And these events have increased in my work, which is why a lot of my colleagues—those composers who have stayed abstract—do not like it at all. In *Hymnen* one hears all sorts of events. Not only national anthems, but there's a shop in China and the reception of a queen in Africa—you hear chariots passing by and the crowd is shouting and singing some tune. I have tried to integrate, through certain technical processes, these found objects into my music. Because I was attracted intuitively by certain events that I couldn't compose myself—events that happen in the acoustic scenery of the planet—and I would like that they are part of my composition; not in a rough way, but through mediation between abstract figures and concrete figures.

'One should be open to what exists, but the main goal of the composer should be that the original part of every composition is much stronger than the quotes and the cliches. If you make quotes you must place the known into a context of the unknown, where the unknown is much stronger and much more fascinating and mysterious—and unidentifiable in the beginning, so that it takes generations to make sense of what someone has composed as new music.'

Birmingham, July 1992

Brian Ferneyhough

Socratic faxes

Brian Ferneyhough

TO: Brian Ferneyhough, University of California, San Diego
FROM Andrew Ford, University of Wollongong
DATE: 28 May 1992

I am preparing a book of interviews with composers and I would very much like to include you among them. I will not be in the United States again this year, but I will be in Europe during late June and England in early July. Will you be going to Darmstadt this year? Are you likely to be available in Europe beforehand? I fly back here to Australia on 16 July. Alternatively, we could do a correspondence interview, but most of the interviews I read with you seem to be of this nature. I suppose at least the fax machine might speed things up and possibly allow for a degree of informality . . .

TO: Andrew Ford, University of Wollongong
FROM: Brian Ferneyhough, UCSD
DATE: 8 June 1992

Thank you for your recent fax. Whilst I am quite prepared to take part in your project, I fear that our various travels will not coincide: I will not be in Britain this summer, and only arrive in Europe at all (for Darmstadt) a day or two before your departure for Australia. Under the circumstances, a fax exchange would certainly be possible—in fact, since my primary theoretical vehicle is the 'written interview' (on a *much* more modest level, resembling the conventions of the Socratic dialogue), I *prefer* such an approach to any (inevitably rushed) conversation. I don't revise much, so texts retain pretty much my spoken 'tone'.

TO: Brian Ferneyhough, UCSD
FROM: Andrew Ford, University of Wollongong
DATE: 21 September 1992

I hope you had an enjoyable summer and trip to Darmstadt. I have put together some questions for you. I'd be grateful if you could make your answers as 'spontaneous' as the fax machine will permit. I am under considerable pressure for space. You may, therefore, wish to take this opportunity to edit yourself, rather than risk possible misrepresentation (which, of course, I would make all efforts to avoid). If there are questions you find uninteresting, by all means ignore them. If I have any supplementary questions, I will fax them back to you as soon as possible in an attempt to preserve the semblance of conversation.

TO: Andrew Ford, University of Wollongong
FROM: Brian Ferneyhough, UCSD
DATE: 23 September 1992

I have contrived to keep well within your size limit. I hope that this is an advantage . . . how 'natural' it sounds is a moot point; it was all composed in a single four-hour period, anyway . . .

AF: Let me begin with a personal observation. I first came across your music in the mid-1970s, via scores such as *Time and Motion Study III* [1974], the *Missa Brevis* [1969] and, a little later, *Transit* [1972–75]. I found them fascinating, but, at the time, utterly inscrutable. Soon after, I began to hear broadcasts—I recall the first performance of *Transit* and also a performance of the Sonatas for string quartet [1967], which I followed with a score. When I finally heard some pieces 'live', I was quite unprepared for their emotional impact: even the solo flute pieces had a very physical, gutsy presence. Clearly, I don't expect you to be able to account for the effect of your music on me, but I wonder whether you might care to comment on its physicality. To what extent do you intend (hope for) an emotional, 'gut level' response to your work?

BF: For me, sound has always been primarily an extension of physical presence, or else physical presence has always been strongly inferred by sound. I assume that sonic contouring is, among other things, a metaphor for bodily comportment and its associated aura of emotive connotations: this makes the 'grain' of sound a tremendously powerful compositional tool. Even the experience of time manifests itself to me largely in terms of degrees of resistance to the free flow of discursive energy, so it's clear that performer mediation and articulation of this aspect of things lie at the root of the listening experience. It's not the inchoate, 'gut' reaction I'm particularly after, though—although that can, of course, differ from piece to piece. That's why I chose 'mediation' and 'articulation' as being descriptive of, and underlining, the intervention of the interpretative intellect in the act of communication.

AF: Your music has been described as showing 'every sign of synthesising a final *ne plus ultra* of orthodox avant-garde conservatism' (Franklin, P. *The Idea of Music: Schoenberg and others*, London, 1985). Is there any sense in which you feel conservative?

BF: It's pretty difficult to say, today, what might *count* as conservative traits, don't you think? In a way, it's amusing to observe the intricate dance of signifiers—even strictly nonsensical terms like 'orthodox avant-garde conservatism' take on a certain whimsical life of their own if bandied about enough. The continual accretion of such sclerotic verbal emblems is *so* much more comfortable than paying attention to the frequently ambiguous and fleeting messages coming from new works of art that one of the main tasks facing us remains that of keeping alive precisely those musical qualities working to destabilise and critically reflect in the gross misuse, for power or profit, of our extant channels of communication. I would think that *anyone* working to construct a personal stylistic ambience today is going to appear pretty anachronistic and conservative, if only because of the underlying (perhaps romantically naive) assumption that the *individual subject* as such is more than a convenient and comforting sitcom fiction kept alive by the culture industry for its own manipulative purposes.

AF: What do you understand by the term 'post-modern'?

BF: Everything and nothing. As far as I can make out, it seems to stand for some sort of symbolic society in which the Hegelian 'grand narrative' has been succeeded by something approaching Schoenberg's theosophical directionlessness à propos *Die Jacobsleiter*. If so, what an irony!

AF: Who are today's musical radicals? How can you tell?

BF: Even marginalisation has been house-trained to Radical Chic. Little is left of the old conjunction of Style and Idea—now it's more like Style and Design. If true, this means that *attitude* cannot be its own sole authentication. What is first of all needed is radicalisation of the work-immanent context—the concrete manifestation of the vision that material, treatment and form are one, and are inextricably linked as interdependent partial facets of a mutual support system. You cannot any longer recognise radicals by *style*, nor, I suppose, by *content* (since the means chosen to articulate that content are usually depressingly reactionary). To me, that seems a positively liberating situation, open to lots of possible individual solutions, even if not many have, as yet, been obviously forthcoming.

AF: It is surely not a coincidence that you have employed a Lisztian title on more than one occasion: *Etudes transcendentales* [1982–85]; *Funérailles* [1969–77]. I find it hard to believe that his music is a particular passion of yours; what attracted you to his titles?

BF: Well, you're right about me not being very close to either the man or the music. At the same time, though, there *is* something fascinating and troubling about such major transitional figures—I mean by that the sense of multiple or alternate realities coexisting at one and the same set of coordinates. There's something shadowy and provisional about even the most intense statements—in fact, they're the works which somehow go most magnificently against the grain of prevailing 'reality'. Perhaps that's why I chose *Funérailles* as a title; certainly, that's part of the reason for the transcendental reference in the *Etudes*.

AF: Are you—again, I suppose, like Liszt—attracted to virtuosity for its own sake?

BF: No, quite the opposite actually. Although it saves time and frustration if a performer commands a virtuoso technique at the outset, any tendency towards superficial brilliance is only likely to hinder appropriate interpretation. I'd say my music was more *anti*-virtuoso in intent, since it takes a very special sort of person to put both their professionalism and their 'natural' approach to their instrument on the line when passing through the early stages of the sort of learning process that much of my music demands. In each case a very personal *key* has to be found in order to begin the task of reunifying the uncoupled planes of mental perception and bodily reaction offered by the score.

AF: Your work is often mentioned as a reference point when discussing the relative complexity/simplicity of today's music. Do you seek complexity? If so, why?

BF: You don't need to *seek* complexity; it's all around you! If my music is 'complex' in intention, it is not because its structure is necessarily more inherently complex than any other music, but simply because the *fact* of complexity is treated as one of the objects of the discourse itself. Perceived complexity is a function of perspective—that is to say, the greater the distance your 'mental ear' adopts to the sonic object, the less 'complex' (the more general in effect, the greater the discrepancy between contributory detail and overall image) that object is perceived to be. The converse is also true: force the ear into the interstices of even a single sustained pitch and it begins to distinguish all sorts of extremely subtle secondary activity. I'm much concerned with that thin line separating a sense of order, however provisional, from temporary disorientation or chaos—I deliberately seek it out, in fact. This means, though, that there have to be a certain number of alternative or complementary backup systems in operation in order that the ear can have the chance to refocus on some other level of the discourse in a way approximately analogous to that employed already— perhaps at a completely different speed or intensity, or else counterbalanced by a more immediately obvious secondary formal function, and so on, but still present. Constantly being reminded of this multivalency of perception can be disorientating, I know, but I am convinced that it is one of the areas of current research most needful of being brought to aesthetic expression.

AF: Typically there are as many as half a dozen different pieces of data for each sound in one of your pieces: pitch; dynamic; timbre; articulation; placing, with regard to rhythm and tempo (which, in any case, is frequently fluctuating). Whilst this may be true of many other pieces of music, comparatively few composers vary these data with the frequency and speed that you do, often from note to note. How do you intend this to affect the sound of your music?

BF: I mentioned earlier the question of *resistance* to the linear flow of information as a significant factor in evoking the physicality of the musical experience. This could be broadened to embrace the general ideas of *interference* and *dissonance* as dynamic formal principles. The secondary articulation quanta you refer to are there, in part, to set up matrices of relationships for the performer which partly offer the prospect of consistency and order, partly conspire to suggest alternative readings or priorities. All these bits of information are traces or echoes of the (now absent) creative act, and thus provide significant clues as to how to avoid overly simplified 'holistic' interpretations. The text is at once one and many, and that is the effect that should be emphatically communicated.

AF: The bass clarinettist Harry Sparnaay said that you were far happier with an imperfect, but urgent live performance of *Time and Motion Study I* than with a carefully detailed studio recording in which just about every nuance was perfectly realised. This suggests that you are not particularly interested in hearing the details in your scores—that you are, perhaps, more concerned with how those details affect the performance of the piece as a whole. Is this broadly true?

BF: Not at all! I wouldn't write details which I didn't think contributed significantly, in one way or another, to the overall richness of discourse. The problem with studio recordings is not that they offer too much irrelevant detail, but that the sense of middle-ground interaction of formal units is sacrificed to editing procedures of a quite different order. I like performances in which the accumulated psychic and

physical momentum of successively confronting lengthy spans of material lends the interpretation an unearthly radiance—the performers
themselves are changing before our very eyes. This is missing from even
the most committed studio recordings (or is, at least, weaker, depending
on specific recording procedures), and there have been times when I
have been prepared to accept the relative imprecision of a live performance as a means to ensuring its presence. This doesn't mean that I
espouse the 'meat-cleaver' approach, though! I've seen a lot of scores
in recent years in which I've felt that the notational complexity doesn't
stand in a compelling relationship to the effect intended: that's a
problem that composers have to sort out with their own performers,
and I can understand why the views expressed in your question have
become common currency in some quarters.

AF: There is a moment in *Transit* where you abandon the precise
notation of pitch. What was the reason for this?

BF: I do this in other pieces too, notably *Sieben Sterne*, and there is
usually some specific point being made. I have always rejected the idea
of notation being a lifeless tool for getting down sounds on paper. It's
a much more complex and active relationship than that. In *Transit*, in
particular, the passage you refer to is the central large tutti, and the
distribution of previously extremely precise types of notation into the
flux and 'putrefaction' of this section stood, in my mind, for some
mammoth 'meltdown', some stage of non-identity which the piece had
to get through in order to survive to the end—a sort of undifferentiated
nourishment or sustenance, perhaps? There were parallels in my mind,
too, with seismic disturbances (lava flows) and alchemical processes,
the literature [on] which I had been investigating at the time.

AF: One broadcast of your work which made a great impression on
me was Abbado's performance of *La terre est un homme* [1976–79]. Are
you still attracted to the orchestra?

BF: Yes, but I don't get the impression that orchestras are attracted
to me. When you have worked a lot with soloists and small-to-medium
chamber ensembles, where you can talk to practically each individual
performer, it is difficult to compose for large, institutionalised groups
of performers who don't really want to play your music anyway. More
than most other formations, the symphony orchestra demands to be
'fed' with works tailor-made to the rock-hard infrastructural givens
dictated by its size and organisational exoskeleton. Either you comply
with those givens, or you rely on a conductor spending half his time
deflecting aggression rather than rehearsing the piece, and no one is
satisfied. My present view is that contemporary music is being enlivened
far more by the incredibly active 'subculture' of committed ensembles

eking out a fragile existence throughout Europe and elsewhere than by the more overt publicity garnered from the odd orchestral performance.

AF: Most of your music seems to find its early impulse in literature, poetry, philosophy or the visual arts. Does the prospect of writing for the stage interest you?

BF: I've been asked that more than once and have never come up with a satisfactory answer. I suppose the answer would be 'yes, but . . .', in that it would depend on coming up with a scenario corresponding with my own sense of how concept, word and music might usefully interact. The practical problems attached to such a venture are immense, of course, not to speak of the investment of energy over a period of years. The fact of often being inspired by non-musical influences does not, of itself, imply an attachment to entire extra-musical contexts. 'Inspiration' often comes about in a piecemeal way, finding succour in dark corners and incomplete or faulty source information, so that such large-scale narrative content as my music might suggest might perhaps prefer to remain decently hidden in the spaces *between* works.

AF: Presumably you became a composer through first listening to music. What were the important pieces? Are they still important? Have other works replaced them?

BF: They're still pretty much the same, even though I now have a better grasp of what specific musical qualities led me to them in the first place. Varèse's *Octandre*, first of all, then some Schoenberg and Webern. Alongside that came a lot of Sibelius, particularly the seventh symphony and some of the tone poems and, slightly later, the Bartók quartets, particularly numbers 3 and 4. As for older music, I was extremely attracted (as I still am) to the Venetian school circa 1600. Monteverdi, in particular, grew on me with the passing years and still remains extremely important. Later came the period from Machaut up until the English Reformation, in particular the Eton Choirbook composers and Tallis. I am still engaged in exploring some of the odder corners of certain national schools and compositional techniques, although I don't think that that has any direct influence on my own creative work.

AF: Do you listen to much music today? Would you describe yourself as a 'music-lover'?

BF: Not, I suspect, in the sense you mean it. I do listen to music, but not on a daily recreational basis. I am appallingly sensitive to ambient noise when composing, and that carries across into leisure activities like reading. I find that music is such a powerful influence on somatic mechanisms that all of one's activities tend subliminally to 'tune in' to what is being heard. It's difficult not to feel like a puppet on a string under such circumstances.

AF: It is almost as hard to credit that you once studied with Lennox Berkeley as it is to believe that Stephen Sondheim took lessons from Babbitt. What do you recall of your work with Berkeley?

BF: Well, what I really like about composition teaching is that it is always changing its definition to fit the prevailing circumstances. It's a wonderfully subjective (but nonetheless rigorous) discipline. I find it difficult, at this distance, to remember particulars of my visits to the Berkeley household. We scarcely ever looked at my music, that's for certain. On the other hand, Berkeley was an extremely refined and cultured man, with the notable virtue of great tolerance for viewpoints very alien to his own, so that our conversations never lacked for content. One year of weekly visits was clearly not long enough to bridge the vast gap between us, but the careful and delicate attempt was probably fruitful in quite unexpected ways, not least of which, in later years, was my own attempt to define the role of the teacher more precisely.

AF: You've gained a strong reputation as a teacher of other composers. Can you describe your approach? What do you look for? What happens when a student comes along who only wants to write in C major?

BF: The first thing I would do would be to ascertain if he understood that he was not writing in C major but rather 'C major'—not expressed as baldly as that, of course. I conceive of the teacher's task as finding out what the pupil wants to do and then helping him to do it better. It is not a legitimate part of my task to suggest that some idioms are inherently more appropriate than others: all one can do is ensure that pupils are sufficiently aware of the implications and ramifications of their choices. The best thing that can emerge from the encounter is that the young composer develops an autonomous critical faculty to replace that artificially provided, for a time, by the teacher. The worst imaginable circumstance would be that the teacher force feed a gifted individual up to a high level without ensuring that such inner autonomy has been reached, since, after a while, a pupil is not able to sustain that early intensity of development.

AF: Your music has been described as 'maximalist'. Does minimalism hold any interest for you at all?

BF: All music needs to work as radically as possible with the absolute minimum of means necessary to do the job. If I feel that these criteria have been reasonably met, I am ready and willing to listen to almost anything. Style is not the issue, in any case.

Liza Lim

No beginning and no end . . .

Liza Lim

Liza Lim lives in Melbourne, I live in Sydney. I had wanted to talk to her for some time about her increasingly distinctive music. Such is the tyranny of distance (and of schedules) that our meeting occurred one sunny June morning in Amsterdam, on the Weesperzijde bank of the Amstel river.

This choice was not entirely random. As we sit at the sidewalk cafe attached to De Ijsbreker—Amsterdam's principal contemporary music venue, where both of us have had music performed—the Dutch bass clarinet virtuoso Harry Sparnaay (responsible for some of those performances) rehearses in the performance space indoors. And on this sunny, windy morning, Weesperzijde has become an ad hoc meeting place for Australian musicians: at the next table to us sits Daryl Buckley, the director and guitarist of Melbourne's Elision Ensemble (and Lim's husband); a taxi cruises to a halt, and out clambers the composer Gerard Brophy. So our surroundings are not so very foreign after all.

Liza Lim's rise to prominence has been of the meteoric variety. Now, she will hate reading that sentence, true though it is, for Lim is cautious when it comes to discussing her career; it is as though she has had tattooed on the back of her hand: 'You are only 26, anything can happen.' But the fact remains: she is going places.

I began to hear of her music (that is, before actually hearing it—that Melbourne/Sydney thing again) when Lim was still a student in her teens. Lim is an extremely self-critical composer and reels in such horror at the mention that I have a cassette of some of those works that I suspect she might be willing to pay a large sum of money to get it back. Her more recent work, however, is quite evidently an extension of those early pieces; she seems to have known forever what her central compositional concerns were to be, and her music since her student days has evolved, rather than changed, into the lyrically tough, sinewy style that characterises works such as *Garden of Earthly Desire* (1988–89), *Voodoo Child* (1989) and the new string quartet *Hell* (1992).

This last piece is her second quartet and, what's more, her second quartet to be played by the renowned Arditti String Quartet. Earlier this year she received a commission from Pierre Boulez's Ensemble InterContemporain in Paris. Given that less than ten years ago she was still a pupil at the Presbyterian Ladies College in Melbourne, I am interested to learn just what her early musical experiences were like.

'I really wasn't at all involved in music in my early childhood,' she admits. 'I did the usual piano lessons and hated them. But my high school had a very active contemporary music program. I remember my first lesson really clearly: the first music I heard was by Penderecki; we were also played Bob Dylan and some free jazz and Aboriginal music and Berio's *Visage*.' (I silently vow that if I ever have a daughter I will move to Melbourne.)

'I thought, "This is music." It was like a key being turned, and I decided to be a composer that day. I was 12.'

Lim found herself composing music for her fellow students to perform, a pragmatic approach which has remained a part of her make-up as a composer ever since. At the Victorian College of the Arts she did the same, and many of those fellow students now constitute the Elision Ensemble—so she is still writing for them.

'Elision operates like a family,' she says, 'because there has been this long-term commitment to the same bunch of people. Having written four works for them—and now I'm writing another—there's a sense in which an interpretive tradition has formed, and the way in which they play in turn influences the way I hear my own music. It's actually a little bit difficult to see where one ends and the other begins, whether the music comes from me or the musicians.'

The plethora of musical styles in the concert hall today has come about partly because so many composers are dissatisfied with the serial and post-serial techniques of the 1950s and 60s. But at least, until about 20 years ago, a student composer knew what modern music was (and also what it wasn't). Today it is almost impossible to be sure, and composers of Lim's generation cannot have had the benefit in their student years of stylistic certainty. I asked her whether she had found it necessary to choose between styles; to ask herself whether she was going to be tonal or atonal, minimal or maximal, experimental or conservative.

'No, I don't think it's a matter of choice,' she replies. 'Obviously one is the product of various confluences of experience, but I don't think there has ever been for me an act of conscious choice.'

But Lim's music, nonetheless, inhabits a very striking stylistic ambit; she is clearly one sort of composer and not another.

'What do you mean exactly?' she asks.

By now interviewer and interviewee are (metaphorically) pacing around each other. I am trying to find a way of pinning the label 'new complexity' on the composer. The composer, understandably, is performing a series of elegant deflections. And we both know it.

'Well,' I wheedle, 'you don't write music like Arvo Pärt, do you?

Or Philip Glass? In fact there are lots of composers you don't write music like. But there are some others with whom I am tempted to link you. Was it ever, for you, a question of taking sides?'

'Well, it's certainly not the "moral" choice which the phrase "taking sides" implies,' Lim explains, as though gently scolding a naughty child, which is exactly how I feel. 'The composers that I feel the closest to are, on the one hand, those who are involved in a very fine and detailed apprehension of sound—and of the inner life of sound—composers like Nono and Scelsi and Lachenmann. And then there are also composers who work with multi-layered, labyrinthine structures, like Ferneyhough, I suppose, and Richard Barrett . . . and Gesualdo!

'But I am very concerned with the performer. With regard to my attitude towards so-called musical material, I think more and more there are no abstract pitches and rhythms, but instead there's an incredible specificity of a particular action which will make a particular sound, and which involves a particular confluence of physical action and tension. I think my music is a kind of observation of that, in connection with its realisation in rehearsal and performance. It's the point at which the sound is made—and the physicality of that—which is where the music happens. Perhaps the music I write is creating spaces in which these points of contact can resonate.'

I ask Lim about how she begins a piece, and how the stream of requests for new pieces affects her writing.

'I find it funny that music can be compartmentalised in that way—you know, you receive a commission, you write the piece and it's performed—because in reality there's just this unbroken flow which results in pieces: there's no beginning and no end either.'

'So,' I ask, 'what if you're asked to write a solo piano piece? How would you begin, do you think?'

'Well, I would never write a solo piano piece,' Lim replies, somewhat disarmingly. 'I've only ever written for piano once, and that was as part of an ensemble. The reason I wouldn't write for piano is that I have a problem with it as an equal-tempered and fixed-pitch instrument, because the kinds of sounds that I like are sounds that are very mobile, sounds which glide—that's why, for instance, there are a lot of glissandi in my work.'

'Okay,' I try again, 'so that was the worst example I could have picked. But say you've been asked to write String Quartet No.3: how do you begin that?'

'Well, I play the violin and was involved very strongly in the string quartet literature. So, on the two occasions I've written string quartets, I've tried to deal with the genre, with its strong performance tradition and compositional tradition, and to try to write works which did not belong to the classical, argumentative, discursive tradition, but instead I tried to look at the string quartet as a single sounding instrument. It's rather as though I were treating the quartet as a gong, and trying to hear all its possible resonances. The recent quartet, called *Hell*—which has a very provocative English meaning, but which also means "light" or "clear" in German—I saw as a challenge to write an anti-heroic string quartet. It was written for the Arditti Quartet, and I wanted to write something which didn't immediately fall within their performing tradition. For instance, there are things like diagonal bowing which produce very unstable sounds and noises and an uncontrollable tone—I call it "beginner's bowing technique", because it's like they've never played their instruments before. This is what I mean by "anti-heroic".'

Amongst the other unusual bowing techniques in the quartet is the instruction for the Ardittis' cellist to bow on the wrong side of his strings—not the wrong side of the bridge, but actually beneath the strings, so that, because of the arched nature of the bridge, the bow only has contact with the first and fourth strings. These techniques are by no means meretricious; they are linked to the unstable, 'unquiet' nature of the piece as a whole, as the composer explains.

'There's a structural ambiguity in *Hell*. One is never sure whether things are beginning or ending, so the piece is non-discursive too. I have this picture of the quartet as a kind of Chinese box—those trick boxes, which you attempt to open, and you think you have, but it's always an illusion.'

So Lim's attitude to commissions, like Stravinsky's, seems to be that they should be made to fit what she already wants to do. That was certainly the case with *Hell*.

'I'd wanted to do that piece for a long time, and then the opportunity presented itself. I had a really clear idea of a piece which was white on white, or silver on silver, and which would contradict its English title, because it's not a hot and fiery hell at all, it's an icy cold one.

'I think I write in a very intuitive way. These days I hardly ever set up pre-existing structures; everything's constantly being modified. I can't think in terms of "here's one note and here's another" because as soon as you have the second note it creates a different context.'

Lim's *Garden of Earthly Desire* is an ensemble piece of great ambition for a composer of any age, let alone a young one. It is nearly half an hour of continuous music, ever shifting, ever reinventing itself, seemingly never going back. The ensemble is dominated by an electric guitar, and Lim's success at integrating that sonority in her eleven-piece chamber orchestra is in itself remarkable. Very frequently the presence of that instrument in a 'classical' setting produces little more than a series of incongruous, anachronistic cliches; here, however, the guitar blends with the acoustic instruments, particularly the soloistic oboe, now impersonating their timbres, now distorting them. In fact Lim's facility for dovetailing, if not disguising instrumental sonorities is one of the most characteristic features of her work.

'That's been one of my preoccupations,' Lim agrees. 'In *Voodoo Child* it's even more extreme than in *Garden*: very often you don't know whether it's a piccolo or a cello or a trombone which is playing.'

Throughout our conversation I was aware of the contrast between Liza Lim's self-effacing manner (she kept apologising for making no sense) and the specific, illuminating answers she gave. She seemed to speak in much the same way that she composes: constantly asking questions of herself, constantly trying to pin things down, frequently managing to do so with considerable finesse, and then sliding off on another, related train of thought.

During our morning coffee in Amsterdam, Liza Lim told me an anecdote about her listening habits which, it later occurred to me, also displayed her quirky, questing imagination. It concerned what happens when she listens to recordings of early music.

'You'll probably think this is really bizarre,' Lim warned me, 'but I have these weird fantasies when I'm listening to this music—particularly lute music—where I'm constantly constructing different versions of it, different directions in which the music can go. I suppose it's this idea, again, that nothing is fixed. I hear Dowland in this way, for instance. Perhaps it's also a game that I'm playing, where I imagine that after this cadence the music could go off in that direction, then it continues, and then I modify it again in my imagination. Do you think that's bizarre?' she asked.

'Pretty bizarre,' I had to admit, '—and Dowland must be a perpetual disappointment to you.'

'Well, if Dowland's a disappointment,' the composer responded, 'Gesualdo certainly isn't, because he actually *does* all those wild things I imagine.'

Amsterdam, June 1992

Nigel Butterley

Flying alone

Nigel Butterley

Nigel Butterley appears to relish quiet domesticity. On the morning I visited him, the quietude had been disrupted by a builder coming to discuss the composer's new kitchen, a project which implied that disruption would escalate. We sat in Butterley's front room, surrounded by art work that seemed vaguely familiar and that, upon closer inspection, turned out to include a John Cage lithograph, an Andy Warhol and a Roy Lichtenstein.

Nigel Butterley's star is rising significantly. His music is slowly starting to re-establish itself in our concert halls. There is no composer in Australia whose work is held in such high regard by every faction amongst his colleagues; every composer in the country seems to admire Butterley's work. But his music has not always captured the public's imagination to the same degree as that of his contemporaries, and since the 1960s Nigel Butterley has increasingly been omitted from the short list in popular discussions of Australian music.

In the beginning there was Sculthorpe, Meale and Butterley. The 'beginning' was about 1963, and there was not much popular discrimination between these three 'experimentalists', 'avant-garde-ists', 'young Turks' or whatever the description might have been. Things then became clearer. Sculthorpe—thanks to a London critic in 1965—became 'the voice of Australia'; in the public's eye, and somewhat to his dismay, he remains this. Meale, on the other hand, appeared to be the very model of a European avant-garde composer—not only did his music seem, on the surface, to fit the tag, but he could even pontificate like Boulez. In the late 1970s all that changed, and (for the public) Meale became overnight the champion of new romanticism. Doubtless both Sculthorpe and Meale cringe at such oversimplifications and wish that public appraisal of their work went a little deeper. Nigel Butterley, on the other hand, has had a different problem: he never fitted—even superficially—into any pigeonhole. Such is 20th century consumerism, that the inability to be categorised leads to neglect.

But this was before the 'new spirituality' of the late 1980s. Nigel Butterley may not like it, and it is certainly glib, but, mark my words, in the next few years we will hear his music associated more and more with this development. His name will be linked to those composers—especially in Eastern Europe—whose music is modal, outwardly simple, yet somehow profound. And if it means that we will hear more of Butterley's work because at last he can be categorised, this cannot be altogether a bad thing. Butterley himself might be thought to be helping this development on its way by singling out composers such as Arvo Pärt, John Tavener and Henryk Górecki for praise. However, it is not, he says, that he wants to write music like them, but that he aspires to their clarity of utterance.

Whatever Butterley's music might be, it has never really been aggressively modern (as Meale's was once considered), nor aggressively Australian (as Sculthorpe's is still under pressure to be). I asked Butterley about his feelings on national identity in music.

'I am interested in and respect the new realisation of the spiritual in Aboriginal life, and this is something I would like to read more about. But I don't know any Aboriginal people; I haven't really had any experience of Aboriginal culture. It's not something I would essentially feel a part of, whereas Europe is.'

So what about Asian music? Both Sculthorpe and Meale, in very different ways, have incorporated the music of Japan or Bali into some of their works.

'It's the same with Asian music. Some of it I don't particularly like listening to: the sound of Japanese music I find very tiresome after a while, and *gamelan* I find very boring, I'm afraid. The fault is in me, not the music. On the other hand, I love Indian music, but I certainly don't feel drawn to include it in my own, not even the talas [rhythmic structures] as Messiaen did.'

Butterley says he was 15 when he knew that he wanted to be a composer. He remembers the precise moment.

'I remember standing in the garden—like St Augustine! Why do these things always happen in gardens? Anyway, I was standing in the garden at home in Beecroft, and I just thought, yes, I want to be a composer.

'But in retrospect there were other signs. I started learning the piano when I was a little boy, and I remember sitting up at the kitchen table: late afternoon, the sun streaming in, and it was very hot. I was sitting there with my toy piano and I had music, although I couldn't read it. My name, significantly, was Miss Fairy, and I was giving my mother a music lesson while she was trying to cook the dinner.'

The music which came to be particularly important to Butterley was English music: Vaughan Williams, Bax, John Ireland and a record of Britten's *Serenade* which his father owned. It was not until the 1950s that Butterley began to encounter modernists such as Bartók, Stravinsky and Schoenberg. When he did, he was sometimes excited, sometimes shocked by what he heard. In 1951 the ABC organised a festival of contemporary music at the NSW Conservatorium, with the Sydney Symphony Orchestra conducted by Sir Bernard Heinze.

'There was the first Australian performance of Bartók's Concerto for Orchestra, but also, I remember very clearly Schoenberg's *Ode to Napoleon*, which was played by Malcolm Williamson just before he went to live in England. I had never heard anything as dreadful; I thought it was absolutely meaningless and ridiculous. I was 17.'

Ten years later Butterley was the pianist in the Australian premiere of Schoenberg's *Pierrot lunaire*, conducted by Richard Meale and sung by Marilyn Richardson. Clearly he had changed his mind about Schoenberg's music, but as a pianist, he recalls, the challenge still was enormous.

'I remember very clearly practising a page at home one Saturday afternoon, and the next morning when I looked at it I couldn't remember whether I'd done that page or not. It was just so unfamiliar. But it meant that everything else after *Pierrot* was very much easier.'

Butterley's musical horizons had broadened considerably, thanks partly to his friendship with Richard Meale. But English music continued to stimulate him and, in particular, the heady, sometimes ecstatic, lyricism of Michael Tippett.

'Because I haven't got an analytical, academic sort of mind, I'm drawn to things more through feeling or intuition, and I just responded to Michael Tippett. I don't know how much of his music I'd actually heard—I'd certainly heard the Concerto for Double String Orchestra—but I'd read about Tippett and I just knew that he was someone I would respond to. So I wrote to him and asked if I could have composition lessons—that was in 1962. He wrote back and said that he didn't teach, but he recommended Priaulx Rainier. And I've read since that he always did recommend Priaulx to people when they wrote and asked for lessons; he said "In my opinion she is the best teacher in London".'

Butterley had only a handful of lessons with Rainier, but he describes them as being 'the right thing at the right time'. Her approach to teaching perhaps appealed to Butterley, because it too seems to have been rather intuitive.

'The music that I presented her with was what I'd written up to that time, influenced by Bartók, Hindemith, Vaughan Williams and so on. I knew that I had to explore somewhere else, but I didn't quite know where. I'd made some tentative steps in the direction of writing serial music, because I knew that this was an up-to-date sort of thing, but it was all very arid. So she could see—and this was what she pointed out to me—that what I was trying to do was, as it were, pour new wine into old bottles. She realised that what I needed to do was to be freer and not just automatically follow the shapes that I was familiar with; she helped me to ask questions all the time. It was what I needed.

'*Laudes* [1963] was the first work I wrote after being with Priaulx. She had said that it didn't matter whether I used a note row or not.

In *Laudes* I did use note rows a bit, but after a while I'd get sick of it and the music would just take over. But it was quite useful as a starting point.'

Butterley says that he has always taken his time to absorb things. He recalls that when he attended exhibitions of contemporary art at this period, often in the company of Richard Meale, he was timid of abstraction, whereas Meale would always home in on the boldest, starkest new paintings by John Coburn or Weaver Hawkins. Given his slow change of heart about abstract painting (as with the music of Schoenberg), Butterley now dreams ruefully about his missed opportunities of snapping up artworks for comparatively tiny sums of money.

Butterley's most recent orchestral work, *From Sorrowing Earth* (1991) won many plaudits at its first performances in Sydney last year. It is typical of the manner in which his music evolves, slowly building an unshakable argument, but it has also made Butterley critical of some of his earlier works.

From Sorrowing Earth was clearly always going to be a major piece for its composer. It was his first work for full orchestra in ten years (since the Symphony of 1980), and its theme—a kind of planetary lament—was both apt and urgent, even if the music is mostly gentle. But it also marked a new approach in Butterley's working methods. I asked him how he usually began a piece.

'I'm changing. I used to have a very clear plan of the piece, but I always left it as late as possible before beginning the composition. I would do the vacuuming, the gardening—anything to put off placing the first note on the page. What really helped me to see I should try a different approach was doing the opera [*Lawrence Hargreave Flying Alone*; 1988], because in that work there are a lot of motifs related to characters and these all had to be woven together. It was all so restricting and slow that I thought: "The next piece I write, I'm going to just *start* it".

'*From Sorrowing Earth* was originally going to be in three movements. What I had done was put ideas relative to it in a folder; every time I thought of something—on the train, for instance—I'd put it on a scrap of paper and put it in this folder. I also dated these ideas, and it was interesting to see that there were several thematic ideas which were very similar to each other, even though they were written months apart without any conscious connection.

'When I started writing the piece, in August 1990, I knew how it was going to start and how it *might* progress. And it developed into a single 23-minute movement. To my mind that structure is much more convincing, and works much better than the structure of the Symphony, which *is* in three movements, and where the middle movement seems to just wander around. Now when I *wrote* the Symphony the middle movement didn't seem to wander around—everything was there for a purpose and I'd planned it all—but in actually listening to the movement it seems a bit purposeless. And I want to revise the Symphony, and I also want to revise *Goldengrove* [for string orchestra; 1982] for the same reason. They both need some spicing up and possibly the addition of some new material to give point to the basically tranquil things that are going on. Whereas *From Sorrowing Earth*, I think, has a sense of purpose, and that came from writing without a clear scheme to start with. Obviously as I wrote, and began to get ideas, looking ahead, then a scheme would begin to emerge, but it wasn't as rigid as in the past, and it was more open to change.

'I showed it to Robert Constable when I'd done about ten pages, and he said, "This is going somewhere—very slowly".'

Butterley's new lease of compositional life and his clear-sightedness about his future plans coincided with early retirement from his teaching job at Newcastle Conservatorium. He has also been the recent recipient of a 'Keating' fellowship. It has meant that he can devote much more of his time to composing. It has also given him the opportunity to return to a busier concert schedule as a pianist, including dusting off John Cage's *Sonatas and Interludes for Prepared Piano* in honour of the composer's 80th birthday.

Given the lushness and precision of Butterley's music, given its romantic leanings and, especially, its renewed sense of direction, Cage seems an unlikely figure for Butterley to admire. However, the very thing that appeals to Butterley about Cage is how he challenges the nature of music, and of art in general. Butterley quotes one of Cage's more famous statements: "I have nothing to say. And I am saying it. And that is poetry".

This enthusiasm for the work of someone whom many people still regard as an anti-artist is perhaps best understood in the context of the writers who are important to Butterley, many of whose words he has set to music. To a list which includes Thomas Traherne, Emily Dickinson, John Donne and Walt Whitman—all, like Cage, mystics of sorts—can be added Butterley's latest discovery, the work of the English poet Kathleen Raine.

'About 20 years ago—it might be more—someone said to me that I ought to get hold of Kathleen Raine's poetry, because it would be the sort of thing I'd respond to. Ever since, her name was in my head, and occasionally I'd look in an anthology and never see anything. And then about three years ago in Abbey's bookshop I found a slim edition of her poems called *The Oracle in the Heart*, and I thought they were wonderful. When Tony Fogg asked me to do a song cycle for him and Elizabeth Campbell, I thought that Kathleen Raine would be appropriate.

'I found out that there was a [collection of her] poems published in 1981 which was now out of print. So I rang Nicholas Pounder's bookshop and asked if they had it, and he said that they didn't, but that a friend of his was going to see Kathleen Raine in three weeks.

And that was the first I knew that she was still alive. So I wrote to her and told her what I wanted to do, and she wrote back and gave me permission, and since then the correspondence has just gone on. Each time I've written back, I've thought, "Well she's 83, she's got better things to do with her time than write to me," but each time she writes a wonderful letter. They're like poems.

'I realised that I could find an epigram somewhere in her work for *From Sorrowing Earth*—I like to do that; I like to have something that the listener can focus on. So I wrote to her again and asked if I could use this four-line poem I had found.'

Raine gave her permission once more and Butterley got his epigram. It stands at the head of the score of *From Sorrowing Earth*, but it could equally well stand at the head of his catalogue of works, since it seems to sum up Butterley's entire approach. It evokes the spirit of his music which, as we approach the end of a century of unparalleled violence and destruction, will, I feel, become increasingly important to his listeners. And those listeners will, eventually, no longer require pop-tags such as 'new spirituality' to help then come to Butterley's very personal music.

> Polluted tide,
> Desecrated earth destroyed:
> Yet one green leaf opens for the heart
> The shelter of a great forest.

Sydney, February 1992

John Cage

Illegal harmony

John Cage

Whether John Cage liked it or not—and it seems he didn't care one way or the other—he became something of an icon in 20th century music. A few months before his death, I visited him in the Greenwich Village loft he shared with the choreographer Merce Cunningham.

We sat at a table in Cage's apartment. Between us were my tape recorder, and a scattered pile of handwritten pages containing new mesostics (like acrostics, but with the key word or words running down the middle of the page) based on the words OVERPOPULATION AND ART. Sitting on some of these pages was Cage's cat, Lo Hsa. The apartment was extremely noisy, the sounds of car horns and general traffic, shouting and building work rising from the street below. Throughout our conversation Cage punctuated his statements with a good deal of laughter. It was a wheezy, infectious laugh, and it reminded me of that passage in Eco's *The Name of the Rose* in which laughter is discussed in terms of its dangers to society; the ultimate subversion of authority.

AF: I realise that if I manage to come up with a question that you haven't been asked before, it's going to be a small miracle.

JC: Oh well, don't worry about that.

AF: I assume you don't teach at all any more.

JC: I never did. I taught a class at one time at the New School for Social Research, and the only reason I did it was that my ideas were so obviously different from those generally taught that I was receiving questions in the mail and I decided to make this the place where I answered them. So I taught for two years, maybe three, and I had a rather distinguished group of students. That also happened in the case of Black Mountain College [in North Carolina, where Cage taught at summer schools in the late 1940s and early 50s]; the students at Black Mountain were almost as interesting as the teachers, so that a great deal was accomplished and then spread. All of the students at Black

Mountain became active artists and all of my class members became active in music.

AF: If you had a young student come to you today and say, 'Can you give me advice? I want to be a composer; what should I do next?', would it be possible to give any serious advice?

JC: I would try to find out who he was, and what it was he had to give in the way of music, rather than tell him how to do it. It's not easy to teach. It's not easy to discover who somebody is. We try, and sometimes we are able to help, but we often fail.

AF: The music world today is very, very different from when you began.

JC: Oh yes. I often say that music in this century has produced not a mainstream but a delta with a multiplicity of musical rivers. In fact I would say now that we are certainly an ocean. Today's music is characterised by a multiplicity of ways to do things; not only from a musicological point of view, but from a technological point of view, there's an enormous amount of music being made that all falls within [the category] we used to call 'serious' music, as opposed to popular music. A great deal of this new 'serious' music doesn't require conventional musical preparation. It depends, as far as I can see, on machines such as you're using to take down your words and my words—for secretarial purposes. People exchange cassettes that they make. They produce, in that way, a large musical culture which is not known in the concert world, but which occupies the people who send the things and occupies those who receive them. And some of this work is very good; not to be sneezed at. None of it is written music; it's all done with machines.

AF: A lot of the people who produce these cassettes are not what we would have termed composers 30 years ago.

JC: No, but they are now. They're putting sounds together. Who are we to tell them what to do, or how to do it? It's remarkably like photography. Photography is dependent entirely upon machines, and so is this—well, no one seems to have come up with the word, but . . . 'sonography'?

AF: Could we go back to your own beginnings as a composer? Your own stimuli and early instruction were fairly conventional. Certainly studying with Schoenberg was arguably the most conventional thing any composer could have done.

JC: There were only two things to do at the time, so it wasn't either conventional or unconventional: you could study either with Schoenberg or with Stravinsky or someone moving in one of those directions. We didn't take Bartók seriously. And I chose the one that Schoenberg offered rather than the neo-classicism of Stravinsky, which struck me as not opening new doors but depending on the past. Later, I met Stravinsky, and he asked me why I chose Schoenberg rather than him, and I said something about the twelve tones and chromaticism as opposed to diatonicism. And he plaintively objected. He said, 'My music is also chromatic.' And then he added, 'What I never liked about Schoenberg's music was that it wasn't modern.' And I've thought about that since then, and Stravinsky was absolutely right. Schoenberg would say, for instance, 'Bach did such-and-such, Beethoven did such-and-such, Brahms did such-and-such, and *Schoenberg* did such-and-such,' referring to himself in the third person. So that he didn't think of himself as changing the past, but rather as one who continued the past. My desire, which comes from my father who was an inventor, is, if I can, to make a discovery which is not based on the past, but is in fact new; which solves a problem which had not been solved before.

AF: So you're saying, in effect, that originality is the most important thing for you?

JC: Not originality. I'm not thinking of myself; I'm thinking of the problems of sound and making a discovery. The first one I made, for instance, which I think was important not only to my work, but which has become important to others, is that the most common denominator of music has nothing to do with pitch—that is to say counterpoint or harmony—but rather has to do with time. The reason it is the most common denominator is because it carries with itself the absence of sound. I've since found that there is no absence of sound, that noise is constantly taking place. But nevertheless, I was able to see that time was of more importance to me than pitch. Now I see that any pitches can go together harmoniously, but they don't produce the harmony that was taught in the schools. A harmony results from bringing sounds together willy-nilly. If we think of the harmony that is still taught in the schools, we have to distinguish it from the harmony that we know by just bringing sounds together, say, by chance. We would say that the school is teaching legal harmony, and what we are practising is illegal harmony. Sounds, just by their nature, produce harmony; [they] can't produce anything else but harmony.

AF: Can this be reduced to the musicological distinction between functional harmony and non-functional harmony?

JC: No, because we don't know what the functions would be. Schoenberg said that the function of harmony—the structural function of harmony—was to show the difference of the parts of the composition. But if you're no longer interested in structure—as some people aren't— some people are more concerned with process—then you have no need to separate one part from the other. So what use would harmony be, except that it just plain exists?

AF: You say you're not interested in structure. Are you talking about structure in your musical works, or structure in general? I mean, to what extent are you not interested in these matters?

JC: That's a very good question. I'm not interested in structure. For instance, with respect to society, I'm not interested in government, which could be said to be the structure of society. I'm interested in bringing about a structureless or government-less world. I *can't* bring it about . . . but I can keep it in mind.

AF: So . . . a form of social anarchism?

JC: Exactly. And you have a great history of that in Australia. I forget his name at the moment, but there was a great anarchist who, I believe, lectured every Sunday on the bank of a river in Melbourne. May I get his name? From this book he sounds just marvellous. This is called *Anarchist Portraits*, it's by Paul Avrich. [*reading*] 'An Australian anarchist: J.W. Fleming.' Do you know his name?

AF: No.

JC: Really? Isn't that marvellous! If you read this book, you'll be very proud of him.

AF: Let me tell you a story. I teach a couple of days a week at a university in Australia. Recently, a group of students did a project, working on your *Variations IV*. What I did was to divide the 20 or 30 students into smaller groups, which worked independently of each other, to come up with a set of solutions to the score, and to put together a performance. Some of the performances lasted five minutes, some 45 minutes. Now, of course I'm required by the university to allocate these students grades, and in an attempt to work out what they should each get, I asked them to keep journals throughout this whole procedure, so that I could then read about what they thought, how they'd set about the project, the reading and research they'd done, and so on. One of these students—a composer—decided that the thing to do was to make his journal as random as possible, in the spirit of your music, and to produce his journal by throwing dice. I said that I found this perfectly acceptable, so long as he didn't mind if I threw dice to determine his mark. There are obviously situations where employing random solutions can be problematic, particularly if you are attempting to work within a highly structured society such as that imposed by a university. Do you simply try to avoid these structures?

JC: No. I keep, as you are doing, a sense of humour. We are in the situation of feeling one way, and having to observe certain conventions and rules in another way. And so we live our lives in total inconsistency.

AF: Do you find that stimulating or worrying?

JC: No. I find it a source of humour. Some people get bitter, and that isn't good—I don't think.

AF: Can we return to your music and your early experiences? It's the mid 1930s. You are studying with Schoenberg. And Schoenberg's teaching methods are traditional, conventional and, presumably, strict . . .

JC: Very. He used the same five-note *cantus firmus* for two years.

AF: Okay, traditional, conventional, strict and boring . . .

JC: No. Revealing.

AF: Can you say why?

JC: Well, because he revealed that when you thought you'd found all the answers, you hadn't. And if you *have* found them all, what is the principle underlying all of them?

AF: Did there come a particular turning point with your studies when you said 'No, enough of that; that's not really what I'm interested in; I'm interested in this'? Was there one moment, or was it a gradual realisation?

JC: Well, the change that I've mentioned from pitch to time was very important to me, and came very early after I left Schoenberg.

AF: And came about how?

JC: Through the use of percussion instruments which had no access to pitch, but which allowed me to give a structure to the compositions—I was still involved with structure at that time—just as harmony had allowed Schoenberg to give structure to his music.

AF: When you say 'time', we are really talking about durations?

JC: Yes. At the beginning for me it was the number of measures, and the measures were all of the same length. So I thought of a structure which would have the number of measures that has a square root. Therefore each unit of the whole piece could have the same proportions—be divided proportionally in the same way as every other unit, and in the same way as the whole composition. That struck me—and still strikes me—as being a convincing structure; not personal, but as factual as, say, the structure of a crystal.

AF: It's the kind of structure that you can then pour the music into, like a mould.

JC: Exactly. You could improvise into it . . . or you could 'cassette' into it . . .

AF: The influence of Varèse here was presumably very important, as well.

JC: Yes. It was and it wasn't. It was, because of the material that he was using; it wasn't, because of his very personal—what can you say?—spirit. His pieces all end with a crescendo, and that increasing loudness at cadential points was very, very personal to him. I became aware of his definition of music as 'organised sound', which he made in an article he wrote for a magazine called *The Commonweal*. I had thought of the definition of music as the 'organisation of sound'; I used three words where he had used only two. And so I used his definition rather than mine for that very reason—fewer words. And I received a telegram from him, asking me to desist from using *his* definition of music.

AF: That's very bizarre behaviour, isn't it?

JC: It was very, shall we say, power-conscious, or government-conscious . . . or at least conscious of himself as opposed to other people. It was not anarchist. What he wanted to say, actually—and he made that clear—was that his music was very important, whereas mine wasn't.

AF: Oh, it was as clear cut as that?

JC: Oh yes. It was made clear that he didn't want the two musics confused, any more than you would want some great artist's work confused with some cartoonist's . . . By the way, we became very good friends after that.

AF: Really?

JC: Well, he came always to hear my music; he came to the concerts. And very few other composers did that. Another composer who often came to my concerts was Henry Cowell, with whom I had studied. Schoenberg never came, even though I gave concerts on the west coast that he could have come to.

AF: You've mentioned Cowell, and I wonder whether it's possible to sum up the significance to you of the American experimentalist tradition in general? For example, what was the difference between the American tradition . . .

JC: And the Australian?

AF: Well, I was going to say the Dadaist movement, actually, or a composer like Satie. Is there a difference between them and what happened in America with Cowell and Ives?

JC: Oh, of course. Offhand, I would say that Satie's shift from

Beethoven is more radical than, say, any shift from Beethoven on the part of Charles Ives. There was in fact no shift on the part of Ives; the idea of climax and balance, of complexity and simplicity, continued. Whereas between Satie and Beethoven there is a great break, and it's the break from a music that involves going somewhere and a music which is not going anywhere.

AF: Music which is content . . .

JC: . . . to stay where it is. Amazing! And Satie is more radical [than Ives]. I think this is the great new beginning for music no matter what—cassette or no cassette—after Beethoven. In fact, without Satie we can't do anything.

AF: I'm not sure whether this is a useful distinction to make, but is Satie's music important in its own right, or simply in terms of what it makes possible?

JC: I think the answer is yes and yes. Satie speaks of 'interior immobility' in the introduction to the score of *Vexations*—none of that romantic passion; no governmental pronouncements. None of that.

AF: This leads directly to two areas you have spoken about a great deal over the years, and two ideas which are particularly associated with you. One is the removal of the composer's ego from the composition, and the other is the deliberate avoidance of beauty.

JC: Not making choices.

AF: Yes. Would you see these as related?

JC: Oh yes. Well, beauty has no meaning.

AF: But you can really only avoid beauty on your terms, can't you? You can't prevent an audience from finding something you've written to be beautiful.

JC: There is nothing that is unable to be perceived as beautiful. I think one can say that.

AF: So how can you avoid it?

JC: You can't. You just don't notice it.

AF: So you don't strive to avoid it, then?

JC: How could you?

AF: It's simply not an issue for you?

JC: We change ourselves by changing our perceptions of beauty. And some of us move toward no limitations—or no distinction between the beautiful and the ugly. Wittgenstein said that beauty is what clicks.

Now instead of thinking of it as clicking or not clicking, you could keep a 'clicker' in your pocket, and if something didn't click for you, you could click it—transform it—transform your perception of it so that you would accept it. As the Japanese say in the world of Zen, 'Day, day, beautiful day', which means every day is a beautiful day. So there is nothing to be seen or heard which is not beautiful. And this is also said in the first paragraph of the third chapter of Joyce's *Ulysses*: 'the ineluctable modality of the visible'—then all the things that we can see are suggested; then in the second paragraph: 'the ineluctable modality of the audible'—all the things that we can hear. There's no limit.

AF: Your philosophy of music is very inclusive, isn't it? It doesn't rule anything out.

JC: I haven't wanted to do that. In that sense I think I follow what I understand of the work of Marcel Duchamp, whose willingness to turn anything into a Duchamp was marvellous—he would sign a paper bag and make me wish that I had offered it to him.

AF: In your identification with that attitude of Duchamp there is a kind of paradox, isn't there? On the one hand, it could be considered a form of creative kleptomania—going around appropriating the world and writing your name on it. But on the other hand, it is also a very unegotistical thing to do.

JC: Completely. And it was that way with Duchamp.

AF: Are you attracted by the ambiguity . . .

JC: Of that situation?

AF: Yes. Not just that situation, but also the fact that it is really very difficult to pin any of these concepts down and say precisely what we're talking about—concerning beauty, for instance, which we were speaking of before. Does that ambiguity attract you?

JC: Yes. If you are adamant for one side, you will fight for it. But if you are as adamant for both sides, as you are for one, then there is no fight involved. There's no war.

AF: So yours is an accepting attitude to life, an open-handed one . . .

JC: What in Indian philosophy is called the 'heroic' life.

AF: You're fond of accidents.

JC: I don't call them accidents. I call them chance operations. The word 'accident' suggests to me slipping on a banana peel, which I'm not particularly fond of. But changes in the weather, unforeseen telephone calls, all those things I don't call accidents, but things that happen by chance. And I use chance operations in all of my work by asking questions and getting answers through numbers—through *I Ching* chance operations.

AF: The simultaneous performance of your works—the 'music circuses'—is this a means of maximising the opportunities for chance operations?

JC: No, I think of those two things as being different. I use chance operations as a discipline to keep my likes and dislikes out of the question. I make music circuses in order to open the doors so to speak to musics that I would not have written; to break down the aesthetic divisions . . . something like that. The music circus is a social act; the use of chance operations is an individual action—it has to do with my sense of my own individuality, which I want to make more open. The music circus also does that; not in relation to me, but in relation to society. It's very happy, you know, a music circus, no matter what the different kinds of music are. You can have Beethoven even, without any trouble . . . together with Satie.

AF: Does your music depend upon the collaboration of others?

JC: Well, I have no idea what my music is doing. It's doing one thing in one person, and another thing in another person. So that I can't tell what's happening; I have no way of knowing. The only one who will tell you out loud what happened will be a critic, and for the most part that won't be interesting or revealing, it will simply reveal his likes and dislikes, which you're already not involved with. So it's out of the question.

AF: But what I was really getting at before was not the collaboration of audiences with your music, so much as the collaboration of performers, which your music, for the most part, seems to require. You're not somebody, it seems to me, who has ever been totally committed to the machine. You're more interested in writing music for *people* to perform.

JC: I suppose so. And they're either people I know, or people I don't know. And the people I don't know have no reason really for playing my work. At the present time, they play it—particularly in Germany, but also here—because they're told to play it by those in charge of their organisations. And they don't necessarily like it; on the other hand, not all of them dislike it. Some of them like it; some of them don't. Some of them know what they're doing; some of them don't. And I'm not a person who likes to tell people that they should like one thing rather than another, whether it's my music or somebody else's. So that's a problem for me, particularly this year when I've received many orchestral commissions—to be involved with people I don't know, and to have to tell them to do things they've never had to do before, and how they should do it. I assume, I suppose, that they will be professional [in their attitudes], but I'm always surprised when they aren't—sometimes they aren't. That then surprises me that I should have to take, if not the position of a policeman (which I refuse), then to take another position (which I also refuse), which is that of the advertiser—the one who explains why they should play well.

AF: In other words, you don't want to be placed in the position of having to sell your music.

JC: No, I don't want to. Another person who didn't want to be present at rehearsals was Giacinto Scelsi. He was always surprised—as I am—why, when you write something, isn't your job finished and understood? But unfortunately people don't read carefully nowadays.

AF: I always feel a responsibility to go to a rehearsal if I possibly can. A responsibility to the piece.

JC: But if you have this point of view of not wanting to force people or persuade people or sell the piece, as you put it, what good does it do for you to go to the rehearsal? I'd just remain silent.

AF: But if people are having difficulties with your work . . .

JC: They have no difficulties in finding it foolish. That's their immediate response; and they begin smiling and having I suppose what they think of as a good time. I'm writing it more and more so that they can't have . . . oh . . . *too* good a time. If you recall my *Concert for Piano and Orchestra* [1957–58], the people who first played it—also wanting to show that it was foolish—put in excerpts from Stravinsky's *Rite of Spring*. That would be what I call having too good a time. But I now write in such a way that they won't put in quotations from anything.

AF: How can you militate against this?

JC: By writing single notes; so there are no melodies.

AF: And these are works for *large* orchestras?

JC: Well, there are a lot of these works now, and they move all the way from solos to over 100 players. Because of my age—next year I'll be 80—I have as a result many orchestral works to write, and I am writing them. So that in September there will be orchestral premieres in Frankfurt, Cologne and New York.

AF: You have a great respect for noise . . .

JC: Illegal harmony!

AF: Well there's a lot of illegal harmony in New York City, especially just outside the window here . . .

JC: Yes. And many people have not learned to enjoy it as harmony. I'm surprised at that. They find it nerve-racking. And I have never found a sound to be nerve-racking; not even a burglar alarm.

AF: Just before I came here, I was sitting in a little coffee bar around the corner on 7th Avenue, and in addition to New York City outside the window, and the traffic and so on, there was a jukebox, and a *Space Invaders* game being played . . .

JC: A music circus!

AF: But a lot of the noise of this city is aggressive noise.

JC: I don't find it that way. I can't tell what the purpose [of the noise] is, so I don't connect it with aggression.

AF: But what about people screaming at each other?

JC: I can't hear what they're saying. It's just sound. Beautiful sound. It's true. That's what I feel; I'm not trying to tell you something imaginary.

AF: No, I realise that. And, quite apart from anything else, it's a very healthy way to cope with New York City.

JC: Because of the season [Christmas], I was invited to a dinner party which was rather large. And I was talking with a lady who lives in the city and who likes New York, but who is annoyed by the sound of it. And so she moves away on weekends to the country. I asked her if she had any trouble with the birds, because they make so much noise.

AF: And she didn't, presumably.

JC: No; she likes birds, but doesn't like sirens and so forth. But if she doesn't like sirens and if the noisy silence of New York doesn't [appeal] to her then she won't be able even to begin with modern music.

AF: Your place in that contemporary music world is singular. Your name is known by people who have never heard your music . . .

JC: And who haven't heard any other music either!

AF: Precisely. You have a notoriety.

JC: Yes.

AF: How do you feel about that? Do you think about it? Do you care?

JC: I give no thought to it. I received a very sweet postcard from a very fine pianist in Switzerland. [It said] that my work is here to stay as part of the world of music, and that she looked forward to playing for me soon. She went to excess and said that it would be around for I think 700 000 years . . .

AF: That's very specific. I've noticed that a lot of your music is being recorded at the moment; there seems to be something new on compact disc every other month. Presumably this gives you pleasure?

JC: No; no it doesn't. I don't have a sound system, and so I obtain no pleasure from this.

AF: But are you pleased that people can go and buy a disc of your work?

JC: No; I've always been opposed to records . . . Why do I permit it?

AF: That was going to be my next question.

JC: Because other people insist upon it, and, as I said already, I don't wish to be a policeman. I have told people in my articles and so forth, that the more records you break, the more music you will have. Because ultimately you'll be obliged to sing yourself. I think it's the presence of records which has brought about such an unmusical society.

AF: Do you think they have any uses?

JC: Oh, of course they do, otherwise people wouldn't demand them so much. I would use them for a music circus.

AF: Apart from all of this [the noisy street, outside], what do you listen to yourself? Do you listen to music?

JC: No. I listen to music when I go to a concert.

AF: Which is often?

JC: Unfortunately it is.

AF: And you go because your own work is being played?

JC: Either that or someone whose music I haven't heard. I don't go to hear the same thing over again. Although I would go to hear any Satie replayed.

AF: But you're unlikely to be found at the Metropolitan Opera's new production of Verdi's whatever . . .

JC: Or even Corigliano.[1]

---

1   John Corigliano's opera *The Ghosts of Versailles* had just opened at the Met, where it was the first new work to be commissioned by the company in 25 years.

AF: Because you've *heard* Corigliano?

JC: No; I haven't.

AF: Then, because . . .

JC: I know it must not be interesting; otherwise he would not have been asked to write it. Isn't that clear?

AF: In addition to your general notoriety, you also have a reputation amongst many young musicians as something of a guru. Do you disregard this, as you disregard the notoriety?

JC: I'm afraid I do. This is a very hard one. Because it's in a department, so to speak, in which a guru is not a guru; or a teacher is not a teacher: namely, he doesn't answer your questions. If you ask him whether he's enlightened or not, he'll say something about his back aching.

AF: A number of your colleagues would do little to discourage people from looking on them as gurus. Do you feel that you might have a responsibility to those who would see you as a guru?

JC: I was very unhappy recently in Spain, where I was asked to be on a television program on the subject of Zen Buddhism. There were present two Zen gurus—real ones. And there were about six other people. I was there as a composer involved in Zen. And I became, in that situation, absolutely speechless; I could neither hear nor speak. The languages were multiple and I was wearing earphones which gave translations of questions which were asked physically in one language and heard at the same time in another. It was a very curious, complex situation and I was very uncomfortable . . . Because, at that point, what happened was that I felt the obligation to be a guru . . . Let us hope I don't feel that obligation again.

New York City, December 1991

Gerard Brophy

Forbidden colours

Gerard Brophy

It was not until Gerard Brophy finally walked into the Atrium bar of Sydney's Inter-Continental Hotel (by which time I was halfway down my second glass of chablis) that the irony of our meeting place occurred to me. Prior to its sumptuous renovation, the building had housed part of the Sydney Conservatorium of Music. We were sitting in the middle of Brophy's alma mater.

'I used to have lessons with Richard Toop on the other side of that door,' Brophy explained, indicating a bedroom on the first-floor walkway. As a bottle of Marsanne arrived and a resident trio began to play sugary background music, it all seemed rather unlikely.

Gerard Brophy seems to specialise in late arrivals. He also made a dangerously late entrance to a profession in which youthful promise is increasingly prized, especially by media commentators. Brophy began guitar lessons at 22 and study in composition followed; by the age of 30, Brophy had established a solid reputation as a composer of sophisticated, italianate sensibility, honed and polished in Rome and Siena at Franco Donatoni's 'finishing school'. I asked Brophy what he had learned from Donatoni.

'I suppose I learned that you can write a piece using any idea; that anything can be your basic material; and that it wasn't the material's fault if it turned out to be a bad piece, it was more likely your fault because you hadn't invented properly with what you had been given. Donatoni used culinary images; he'd say, for instance, that you use all of the pig, you don't waste anything. I think that's a good philosophy. I tell my own students that.'

As with many of Donatoni's pupils, Brophy emerged from his period of study audibly influenced by the Italian's musical style and methods, but the interest in Mediterranean musical thinking had predated his study with Donatoni. One of Brophy's most impressive early works is italianate in quite a different way. *Exú* (1982), for amplified solo violin and orchestra, is a virtuoso showpiece, flashing with brilliant flourishes for soloist and orchestra alike.

'That was my Sciarrino piece. I'd heard his *Caprices*, which are modelled on the ones by Paganini, and I thought I have to rip this off and write my own. I wrote the first half before I went to study with Donatoni and the second half after I arrived in Rome, but I had the good sense not to show it to Donatoni until it was finished. He *hated* that piece, he absolutely *loathed* it. He tore it apart in front of everyone. It was like Castro at one of his rallies: he went on about it to the class for two hours—this is no exaggeration—and he was thumping the desk and everything. He said, "There's too much will in it; there's no process in it." At the time, I suppose I agreed with him, but now I don't at all; now I'm much more interested in abstraction without process.

'I look at my Donatoni period as an apprenticeship, and I think it's important to have that—it doesn't matter what your career is. You do your apprenticeship and at some stage your own personality will emerge. I'm not interested in trying to reinvent music. I'm not a Cage. I admire the man enormously, of course, but I'm just not like that.'

The pigeonhole into which Brophy was slotted on his return to Australia was that of uncompromising European modernism. When his music was discussed it was as often linked to names such as Sylvano Bussotti as to Donatoni, but it was a label Brophy always wore a little uncomfortably. Beneath the fast, brilliant surfaces of appropriately named works like *Scintille* (1984) and *Mercurio* (1985) lurked a growing preoccupation with harmony. After the mighty piano concerto, *Le reveil de l'ange* (1986–87), the brakes were judderingly applied to the teeming activity of his earlier scores, and not only did harmonic cogency of a decidedly functional kind begin to appear in his music, but also hints of melody.

'It started with *Seraphita* [1988], which I had to write for the Australia Ensemble when I won the New South Wales Premier's Award. That was the first of these slow pieces. I was sick to death of fast pieces with lots of notes, so I thought I'd write some slow pieces with lots of notes, but fewer pitches. *Forbidden Colours* [1989], which I wrote for the Pittsburgh New Music Ensemble, was even slower, and it's not very modest of me, but I think it works well. I took the central section of a much earlier piece, *Senso* [1982], and expanded it vertically and horizontally. It has an eleven-note melody, but only five pitches—F, F sharp, G, G sharp, A—so there are minor thirds and major thirds. So this set a trend. There have been some faster pieces, like the flute piece *Nymphe-Echo morphologique* [1989] and *Frisson* [1989] for three guitars, but they're minor pieces as far as I'm concerned.

'I'm getting back to melody—that's what I'm aiming at. *Les roses sanglantes* [1991; for bass clarinet and small orchestra] has long, slow lines, without any of that instrumental twitching that you find in *Seraphita*, for example. A piece like *Quartet for the End of Time*—that's very important to me; Messiaen could write melodies and I want to write melodies too. But then I've also been incredibly influenced by people like Ornette Coleman.

'I think there'll be a fairly shocking change in my music in the near future; I think I'm going to do a bit of a Ross Edwards—I don't mean that I'm going to write something like Ross's Piano Concerto, but there'll be a big change of direction.'

Did Brophy feel that these new concerns were always present in his work? What inspired this need for melody?

'It came from writing vocal music. The first piece was really *Shiver* which I did for the Nieuw Ensemble's tenth anniversary in 1990 along with a number of other composers. It was supposed to be very short—Ferneyhough and Kagel's pieces were only two minutes long—but I overshot and *Shiver* lasts about seven minutes. It's a vocal piece and I thought, well, you've got to write a melody for this woman to sing, you can't just write hiccups. I think minimalism is finally making a mark on me.'

This seemed something of a non sequitur, since some of the most famous minimal pieces are distinctly non-melodic, so I asked Brophy to explain.

'It's a general thing. I can't point to specific pieces which have influenced me, but it's to do with using fewer notes; it's to do with focus. My problem with Donatoni's music, say, is that there's not enough of a centre for me. Register's important for me, and pitch centres and also, I suppose, reiteration of material—I'm very interested in repetition, but incomplete repetition, faulty repetition. I don't want to put too much information in the pieces any more; but it's a fine line between too much and not enough.

'Flash virtuosity doesn't inspire me any more. I would never ever write a piece like *Le reveil de l'ange* again. It's too much; it's *expecting* too much. But there's a stratum of pragmatism running through this too, because I'd also like to get a few more performances.'

I asked Brophy whether he could explain why he composed and what he thought his music meant.

'I present an idea, and follow it with a series of possible directions which that idea could take: this is what I've found; this is what I've tried to make out of it. That's it. Nothing terribly profound; it's playing with sound and hopefully expanding people's perceptions of what music can be. But I want it to become more than that, that's what the interest in melody is about. I suppose I'm becoming a little bit more program-matic—not, I hope, in a cheap way, but if I'm dealing with texts, I want to enhance their meanings with music. I heard Henze's *El cimarrón* again the other day—Lyndon Terracini sent me a video of his perfor-mance and I played it for my students—and I hadn't heard it for a long time. What impressed me about the piece was that you could hear what he was singing; if you're going to set a text to music, as far as I'm concerned, you want to *hear* the text.

'I'm not trying to be pretentious, but I feel that I'm coming towards the end of a cycle. And I'm not going to be writing the new music equivalent of Barry Manilow, but I do sense quite a radical shift. The trouble is that people who know your music—I'm talking about colleagues, not so much the average punter, who's much more open-minded—they have certain expectations, and you get the feeling that they want you to do the same thing all the time; they do pigeonhole you. But as far as I'm concerned, it boils down to the fact that I try to write the pieces I would like to hear.'

The other change which appears to be overcoming Brophy's work is in his choice of texts. The 1989 world premiere by Sydney's Seymour Group of his virtually pornographic cantata buffa *Flesh* (1987) created a small sensation. The text was woven from a variety of sources, including classified advertisements from the back pages of New York's *Village Voice*. At one point the baritone soloist sings: 'Retired costumer into water-parties and basinette discipline seeks slender man for evenings of gourmet food, vodka and heavy petting in liturgical settings. Must be acquainted with the later works of Buxtehude.' As a new bottle of Marsanne arrives, the composer explains that his desire to shock is diminishing as fast as his interest in melody is growing.

'The texts that I've chosen, I suppose, do say something about me. In *Flesh* there was the commercial side of sex that I was amused and titillated by: those *Village Voice* personal columns and some of the grosser bits from Louis Nowra's book *The Cheated*. With *Shiver* I used one of Aretino's sonnets. I'd bought an illustrated copy of them the year before in Rome, and thought some of them were quite cute, and also phonetically interesting. The one I set was fairly erotic, and I tried to steer away from this "hard-core" stuff in *Vorrei baciarti* [1991]—I mean the English translation of the Aretino sonnet in *Shiver* is pretty strong stuff; there's a moment when the mezzo-soprano sings: "You can stick it up my bum, but I assure you it will come out clean . . . ".

'I want to steer away from this kind of sensational thing; I'm not so interested any more. You can see all that stuff on the *Donahue* show. Perhaps my prudishness is coming out. I'm looking for better values, quite frankly. I'm sick of pulling my pants down and showing my bum in public. I'm 40 next year, Andy.'

And finally the setting for our conversation no longer seems so very ironic. The noisy Conservatorium of Brophy's youth has become the sophisticated watering hole of early middle age. But if this might indicate that Brophy has gone soft, anyone who knows him will realise that this is simply untenable. Because, even as he is dismissing Phil Donahue, his show and its values, he is displaying an almost encyclopaedic knowledge of the program; as he speaks of not wanting to be so sensational any more, there is a wicked grin beginning to twitch beneath his moustache.

Sydney, May 1992

Michael Nyman

Jerry Lee Lewis plays Mozart

Michael Nyman

Pointing a microphone at someone who has just woken up is most unfair, especially when they have been off a flight from London to Sydney for only a few hours. But Michael Nyman is chatty and keen to do his duty by the people from Decca who have arranged an entire afternoon of similar encounters for him. The fact that a record label, rather than a publishing house, is organising his life says rather a lot about Nyman's career. He is primarily known, these days, as a film composer. When I ask him about his other music he seems pleasantly surprised.

Nyman began composing as a child, although he says he was never very good at finishing pieces. 'There are notebooks lying around at home with lots of beginnings, a few middles and absolutely no ends.'

At the Royal Academy of Music composition was not his principal focus, but in the early 1960s, with four pieces under his belt (all of them performed and reviewed), he attended the Wardour Castle summer school ('a hotbed of post-Webern serialism') where he met the composers Maxwell Davies, Birtwistle and Goehr.

'It was made pretty clear to me that if you didn't write serial music you were just a total dummy, and if you wanted to write music like Britten you might as well not breathe. I sat down and tried to write a twelve-tone piece and it just came out horrible and mangled and it had nothing to do with who I was as a composer. So I went into voluntary exile.'

Nyman maintained his contact with other composers as a friend, a commentator on their work, a critic for the *Spectator* and, in the case of Birtwistle's music–theatre piece, *Down By the Greenwood Side* (1969), as a librettist. He worked for Birtwistle's publisher, Universal Edition, as an editor, but in all this time he says there was never any temptation for him to write music. He also wrote a book called *Experimental Music* and I asked him how this came about.

'It seems very strange, because it was happening under my nose, but I discovered purely by chance the composer Cornelius Cardew. This was 1968 and he was unknown to me. I went along to the Wigmore

Hall to review his piece *The Great Learning*, having the previous night heard some overblown, dramatic piece by Maxwell Davies. Cardew's music was such a relief; it was so psychologically neutral, so pleasant, so unhysterical. And so, without any forewarning, I immediately fell for it and got to know all the composers working in what we then called "experimental music"—Cornelius, John Tilbury, Gavin Bryars, Howard Skempton—and the American composers with whom they were associated: Earl Brown, Christian Wolff, Morton Feldman, John Cage. And through John Tilbury I discovered Steve Reich. And here was a world of music and ideas and structures that was totally new to me.

'So it was 1970. I still wasn't writing music. I put together some concerts for Steve in '71, went on tour with him in '72, organised more things for him in England in '73 and '74. And then in '76 I engineered a dinner between Birtwistle and Reich—I remember Harry made a very spartan Lancashire hotpot—and that was interesting, and I think in some of the pieces Harry wrote after that you can detect Reich's influence.'

Nyman's rebirth as a composer, however, came not through experimentalism or minimalism, but—oddly enough—through Birtwistle, with whose music Nyman had very little sympathy at the time, even though the two had remained friends.

'In 1976 Harry had been appointed Musical Director of the National Theatre, and the opening production on the Olivier stage was Goldoni's *Il campiello*. Harry knew that I'd been a musicologist ten years earlier and so he asked me would I go to the British Museum and dig out some Venetian popular music of that period. So I discovered these mid 18th century gondoliers' songs that had been dressed up as sub-Mozartian piano sonatas, I wrote down all these tunes and I gave them to Harry.

'Then I had a phone call from him asking whether I'd like to write the score. So I said yes, and the task was to discover what a Venetian town band sounded like. Well, I soon discovered that there weren't any—there were itinerant violinists and that was about it.

'So, totally off my own bat, I decided to form this fictitious Venetian town band, which would be as rude and raucous as possible; on the one hand I would use banjo and saxophone, on the other I would use sackbut and shawms and rebecs—early music instruments. It proved very popular and I was excited by the sound of this rackety little band and decided to keep it on and put on concerts. But I was then confronted with the problem of what to play, so I had to start writing music. And I haven't stopped since.'

So the Michael Nyman Band, at least in embryo, was thus formed, but I was interested to know how his distinctive brand of rude minimalism originated.

'The curious thing is that if you'd asked me the night before I started composing what sort of music I was going to write, I wouldn't have been able to tell you. Until I sat down and wrote my first piece I had no idea what I was going to do. I found the sixteen bars from the beginning of the 'catalogue' song from *Don Giovanni*—the chord changes had always fascinated me, they are quite unlike anything else Mozart ever wrote—and I thought I'd use them in my piece. I wasn't thinking, "I'm going to be a post-modernist, I'm going to recycle other people's music", it was just that I loved this thing and wanted to make something out of it.

'So I looked at it and discovered the components of the texture: there were the repeated quavers in the strings; there was the step-like bass part; there was the first violins' imitation of the bass part at the distance of one bar. I thought, "This is an interesting texture, I'll take it apart and put it together again." So I started playing the repeated quaver chords on the piano, but instead of playing them as they're written, I played them like Jerry Lee Lewis. I'd never played the piano remotely like that before and I thought, "Shit! I really like this." So, simultaneously, I discovered an approach to texture, an approach to piano playing, and a piano style which dictated the dynamic, articulation and texture of everything I've subsequently done. It was born in one complete package.'

Following *In re Don Giovanni* (1977), the work that grew from Nyman's obsession with the 'catalogue' aria, came his work for the film director Peter Greenaway. Nyman had known Greenaway for some time and, almost as soon as he began composing, the director began to employ him as a sort of house composer. The film that established both director and composer was *The Draughtsman's Contract* (1982), in which Nyman drew on Purcell; in *Drowning By Numbers* (1988) it was the middle movement of Mozart's *Sinfonia concertante* which provided virtually all the musical starting points. Okay, so Nyman doesn't want to be called a post-modernist (who would?), but what is he? What does he mean by all these musical references?

'What do I mean by them? I find some classical musical materials just fascinating in themselves and they suggest things to me—ways of working. But they're all different. *The Draughtsman's Contract* is twelve ground basses which I made my own, sometimes using Purcell's melodic material, but generally not. In *Drowning By Numbers* everything was taken from that slow movement—I even stuck with Mozart's orchestration.'

But Nyman is at pains to point out that most of his work is neither film music nor based on other scores; indeed, he implies that there is nothing derivative about his score for *The Cook, the Thief, his Wife and her Lover* (1990). Which is fine, except that the processional music does bear an uncanny resemblance to the frost scene from Purcell's opera, *King Arthur*. I put this to him.

'You know I've always been very honest about my source material.

If you read my sleeve notes, I've always said where everything comes from. This time I thought, "Bugger it! People who know the frost music will know it's the frost music." I haven't passed it off as mine, but I haven't admitted it was Purcell. So you're right. You spotted it. I admit it, guv.'

Sydney, September 1991

Barry Conyngham

The fast lane

Barry Conyngham

You might think that since both Barry Conyngham and I work in the same building, it would be easy enough to interview him. However, Conyngham, as Professor and Head of the School of Creative Arts at the University of Wollongong, is usually in meetings; I, on the other hand, as a twice-weekly lecturer, am generally teaching. Our solution to the problem is to record this interview in transit between Wollongong and Sydney; the interviewee drives.

Barry Conyngham belongs to the middle generation of Australian composers that includes Anne Boyd and Ross Edwards. Like them, he was once a student of Peter Sculthorpe. Conyngham is a prolific composer, and when we spoke was preoccupied with his orchestral piece *Decades*, commissioned by the ABC to mark its 60th anniversary. I was genuinely interested to know how and when he finds time to compose anything at all, given his professorial duties.

'Normally, I work a couple of hours every day, before going in to the University—three hours in a day is long for me. But over Easter, I took a week off, and I had fantasies of doing two and a half, if not three of the five movements in *Decades*. As it turned out, I did in fact work very long hours, sometimes up to fourteen hours a day; however, I had this incredibly funny problem with the first movement . . . '

Conyngham's approach to composition has changed little over the last 25 years. He collects musical materials over a long period of time—perhaps a year—and then assembles them quite quickly to produce the final score. *Decades*, in fact, is based on six chords ('well, really just collections of pitches') which, as is usually the case in Conyngham's music, generate most of the pitch material of the work, from melodic lines to harmony. I asked whether he discovers these chords at the piano or simply hears them in his head.

'Yes, I mess around at the keyboard. The sort of chords I like are filled out and polytonal. A typical Conyngham chord, for instance, is E flat, G flat, B flat, C, E natural, F, A, D. As has been pointed out to me by good listeners, this is a kind of jazzy chord; these chords are not too far away from extended, traditional added-note chords. A lot of this is only as conscious as it needs to be in order to get the job done, although it's interesting that if I go back and look at scores like *Ice Carving* [1970], the chords aren't that different.'

So what, then, was the problem that Conyngham's tried and true system ran up against with *Decades*?

'Well, I was writing out the final version, and following quite detailed, but disparate pieces of planning material—like putting together a jigsaw puzzle—you know, that rather lovely term of Patrick White's: oxy-welding. Anyway, I had this feeling of the movement staggering; it was like trying to control a car with a flat tyre.' (Suddenly I am very aware of the composer's driving.)

'I got unhappier and unhappier, and worked longer and harder and generally got to be obnoxious with my family, and by about the Wednesday or Thursday of that week I was really worried. It hadn't happened to me before, that I'd been so unhappy with the sounds that were on the page as against the projections that were in my mind; I usually know exactly what it will sound like—I mean I can sing it through in my head. It was a kind of a crisis, but you keep struggling on because what's in the sketches has taken a year of work and, you know, I have faith in the system. But more and more I got annoyed and finally I thought, "This is bloody stupid".

'I don't often do this, but I sat at the piano and went back to how I would normally—in the *making* of the piece—play through the chords and get the music into my head. I tried to use the piano to verify . . . not what was in the score, but what was in the sketches. And I discovered that the *first chord* was wrong; I had transcribed the first chord of the piece incorrectly and then believed what I'd written. And as soon as I heard it on the piano—bang!: there it was. Then, of course, I had to go back and redo the whole thing. But, in fact, these five or six days of agony became really quite great pleasure, because they verified the integrity of the system; it said to me: "If you have the wrong chord, Barry, all the music won't make sense." I took great comfort in that.'

Barry Conyngham came rather late to composition.

'I had a very strange musical education and a late start as a composer. I'm not sure when I started playing the piano—I was probably 8 or 9. Anecdotally, my mother—who comes from a Scottish Protestant background—sent me to the nuns, because all good Protestants know where the best music teaching goes on. In those days, when a boy reached puberty, he got kicked out of the convent, so when I was 12 I was politely told that I could no longer attend. By the time I was 13 or 14 I had given up doing AMEB exams and so on, because other things—like girls—were becoming more important. But, because of my father and my brother, I discovered jazz. This is the late 1950s.

'I had a band at school and we earned money playing at surf clubs and so on. At Sydney University, where I'd gone to study law, I joined the jazz society and we used to play gigs, and I'd write arrangements and some original material. And I discovered that this gave me great pleasure. Then—suddenly—I heard the Budapest String Quartet play the six Bartók quartets, and it blew my mind that music could be like that.

'I hadn't had any formal music training since the convent, so when I applied to the Music Department I had to do a crash course. I didn't come from a classical background: I heard my first Beethoven and Mahler symphonies in my late teens. Peter Sculthorpe was on a Harkness Fellowship in the States at the time, so he wasn't there in my first year in the department. The first piece I wrote there was a cello sonata—not one of the great pieces, but it had some originality, including a middle movement which was influenced by John Coltrane. Anyway, it was played at a student concert and Peter had just got off the plane and decided to come along to see if there was any talent among the new students. After the sonata was played he shouted from the back of the auditorium, "There is a composer!"'

Conyngham progressed quickly. At 22 he had his choral piece *Farben* performed at the 1966 Adelaide Festival.

'I was absolutely convinced that I was going to be a composer. I started to get a few performances and very quickly I was sort of propelled into the public arena. In 1968 I wrote the orchestral piece *Crisis: Thoughts in the City*, which was my first score to be published by Universal Edition.

'The two pillars of Australian music, of course, were Sculthorpe and Meale, and by now I was copying for both of them; I copied Richard's *Very High Kings*. I remember going to Peter and saying: "You've got the *Sun Music*/texture/landscape market tied up—that's you; Richard is the European-angst/city-dwelling intellectual; how am I going to find a place?" And it was Richard, in fact, who said to me, at three o'clock one morning when we were both pissed, "It doesn't matter who you are—that's all you'll ever be. But you should find out who that is, and stop trying to be someone else." I still tell that to my students. So finally I went to Peter and told him, look I've decided that the city is going to be my thing. And that's what *Crisis* is about.'

The next big step for Conyngham came in 1969, when he met Tóru Takemitsu who was touring Australia for Musica Viva with the NHK String Quartet. Conyngham already knew some of Takemitsu's music, although unlike Peter Sculthorpe and Anne Boyd, he was not particularly interested in including Asian elements in his own work. Takemitsu stayed in Sculthorpe's house and Conyngham had a good deal of contact with him. This resulted in an invitation to study with Takemitsu in Japan.

'When he went home, he left on Peter's mantelpiece an American $100 note on which he'd written "For Barry—you must come Japan—Tóru". I took it to be a sort of down payment on an airfare—and a substantial down payment in those days. Unfortunately I was so bloody poor I had to spend it. But then I went to Tokyo anyway, because of a bit of luck when I landed a contract to do the music for Expo '70 at Osaka; I also got a Churchill Fellowship, which made the front page of the *Sydney Morning Herald* because . . . well, a Churchill Fellowship to go to Japan?'

In fact, Japan provided Conyngham with a wide range of stimuli. Besides his exposure to Takemitsu, he came into contact with Xenakis and Stockhausen, both thanks to Expo '70.

'The West German pavilion was opposite the Australian pavilion, and it consisted of a geodesic dome in which, for twelve hours a day, seven days a week, for six months they played Stockhausen and only Stockhausen. So I met Mauricio Kagel and the Kontarsky brothers. By the time I got back to Australia I could have been the world authority on Stockhausen, because for six months I had literally eaten my lunch listening to his music.'

Conyngham's period in Japan produced his most striking music so far, notably the remarkable *Ice Carving*, for solo violin and four string orchestras, and *Water . . . Footsteps . . . Time*, for four amplified soloists and two orchestras, in which some of the influences Conyngham had picked up were fairly evident: the title of the piece is a version of the title of one of the Xenakis works performed in Japan; the presence of an amplified tam-tam as one of the solo instruments is clearly a result of hearing Stockhausen's *Mikrophonie I*. But, now back in Australia, Conyngham was still coming to terms with what he had absorbed.

'It took me a long time to realise what I had got out of studying with Toru. I was committed to the notion by then of there being such a thing as an Australian music. I got this from Peter of course, and it meant far more than simply writing music in Australia—it implied a music which consciously occupied itself with things that are unique to the country. I was able to draw on the wonderful sense of spaciousness which is in Takemitsu. I also came up with the idea that isolation and loneliness could be seen as a kind of metaphor for being Australian.'

So Conyngham went from strength to strength. Commissions continued to appear, he won a Harkness Fellowship which allowed him to complete post-doctoral studies in southern California and by 1975 he was on the staff of the Music Department at the University of Melbourne. His interest in music–theatre grew and this included dance, culminating in 1988 in the appropriately named *Vast*—one of the few full-length orchestral ballet scores to be composed anywhere in the late 20th century.

In 1989 Conyngham was appointed Professor of Creative Arts at Wollongong, bringing him within a short distance (which, in his car, we have now almost covered) of his native Sydney. Music for the theatre is now being edged out by a steady flow of orchestral works, especially concertos in which the soloist-as-protagonist has, perhaps, assumed the dramatic role.

There is a sense, today, of Conyngham having come full circle and this is partly, at least, what *Decades* is about. In a way, it is 'Volume 1' of the composer's musical autobiography (so far there are no plans for sequels). *Decades* is about the 1960s. The five movements have titles which describe the young Conyngham's progress through that period: it was a time of discovery for many people; in Conyngham's case it was also the discovery of his vocation.

'It's really universal. I mean most people go from adolescence to adulthood; so it's anyone's decade. But also, from my point of view, it's about the 60s—and so it could be anyone's 60s, too. The 60s were remarkable. Because there wasn't just that sense of optimism, it was also a very frightening time. I remember the Bay of Pigs vividly: Kennedy and Khrushchev playing chicken. I had dreams of nuclear explosions off Bondi. Literally, I had these nightmares. I went on CND marches in 1963; I was arrested over Vietnam when Lyndon Johnson came—I wasn't charged, though, I was disappointed. And in 1967 the Aborigines got the vote. And then the '68 riots in America and France. And Kent State in 1970, which is the beginning of the really nasty stuff; I mean we all knew Nixon was a shit, but we didn't quite know the level of what was going to happen. Kent State was scary.'

So now, pushing 50, Barry Conyngham—professor—appears to be taking stock. I suggest to him that in the last few years there seems to me to have been a marked convergence between his music and that of his former teacher, Peter Sculthorpe, especially in the way that each of them seems drawn to composing music which has a sure sense of direction; music that is dynamic. He replies that no one has said that to him before, and he'll have to ponder it.

Why does he compose? What is his motivation?

'Ultimately, for me, music is about guts and intuition; it's not about the intellect. I mean I like my mind and I like other people's minds, but art is about accessing far more than the brain.'

Wollongong—Sydney, May 1992

Richard Rodney Bennett

Nobody does exactly what I do

Richard Rodney Bennett

When not writing what he describes as his 'concert music', Richard Rodney Bennett is often to be found performing the songs of Gershwin, Porter and Harold Arlen in New York piano bars. During the 1990 Adelaide Festival he played a week of cabaret, and after one of these performances I took him to dinner.

AF: You studied composition with Pierre Boulez in Paris. You are a jazz pianist and a cabaret singer. But you are still probably most widely known as a film composer, with scores for *Murder on the Orient Express* [1974], *Equus* [1977], *Far From the Madding Crowd* [1967] and many others to your name. At the age of 22 you composed the music for *Indiscreet* [1958] starring Ingrid Bergman and Cary Grant. Have film scores been a means to an end?

RRB: You know, films always supported me. I mean they allowed me to write the music I wanted to write. Whereas all my friends either taught small children or washed dishes—things that had nothing to do with music at all. In all my life, I never had to do anything that wasn't to do with music. And what I'm doing now—playing and doing cabaret and jazz—is 'cause I love it so. It's a challenge. I don't perform any more as a classical pianist, which I did for many years, because now there are so many people who do it well, and young kids who play Berio and Webern and stuff, as a matter of course. That's why I stopped doing it finally. But this kind of cabaret—regardless of whether it's good or bad—is something that only I do exactly like that.

AF: How long have you been doing it?

RRB: All my life I've been playing tunes. My parents were classical musicians. My mother was a pupil of Gustav Holst, and sang in the offstage chorus at the first performance of *The Planets* when she was 17. And so I grew up in Devon, during the war and afterwards, and music was what we did. I suppose from the time I was about 8, I started picking tunes up off the radio. I didn't know what Gershwin was. I didn't know what Hoagy Carmichael was. But they were lovely tunes, and so I started to play them. Then gradually over the years it became more and more important. And then in 1976, I was working with Marion Montgomery, and I was singing her a lyric of a song that I wanted her to do with me and she said, 'You're going to sing with me on the stage.' Well, suddenly starting to sing when you're a classical musician and a pianist is such a step. I cannot tell you. It's an enormous psychological step. To look at an audience and tell them lyrics. It feels as though you're naked.

AF: You do actually have to act those songs.

RRB: You do. And it is such a challenge, and every time I do this kind of music, some nights I'm good and some nights I do it on automatic. And some nights the audience are dumb, and sometimes they are so bright it's like having dinner with your best friend. And so every night is different and I cannot say it was like that when I was performing contemporary music. You learned to play the piece as well as you could, and give or take a few slips, that was your performance.

AF: You presumably have the ability to compartmentalise your musical activities?

RRB: I've always done that all my life.

AF: They don't seem to bleed into each other at all. I mean the orchestral music you've written doesn't contain jazz. At least I haven't heard any pieces which do.

RRB: No. Athough, having been a jazz pianist all these years, you get a rhythmic sophistication which is enormously helpful in the performance of contemporary music. In the sort of wild days when I was a student, I was one of the first two English pianists to perform Boulez's *Structures*, which is the hardest two-piano piece ever written.

AF: Susan Bradshaw was the other one?

RRB: No, that was Cornelius Cardew, who was my buddy. We were very close, and both of us had a background in jazz. Now, in jazz, you learn to have a sort of internal click going, regardless of whether you're stating it, and that is enormously helpful in playing difficult contemporary music. But I can't say that there is any surface evidence of what I do. I mean I think that my classical music—my concert music—has a certain rhythmic vivacity and tension, but it's not jazz. But I rather like the fact that my life is compartmentalised. A lot of my friends in New York know me as a singer-pianist. And a lot of people—and this I'm less interested in—know me as a composer of movie music. And basically I'm not really interested in movie music. I like doing it. But you know, there are people who think that Dimitri Tiomkin was as great as Stravinsky. That's nonsense. Movie music is journalism, and

Tiomkin was a great journalist, and I was not a bad journalist when I was doing that, but it bears no relation . . .

AF: That was yet another compartment, wasn't it?

RRB: Yes, it was.

AF: Because there is a world of difference between, say, the film score of *Nicholas and Alexandra* [1971] and your orchestral piece *Zodiac* [1976].

RRB: Yes . . . Thank you. Apart from anything else, *Nicholas and Alexandra* was written in about three weeks. The film was finished, I knew the range I could work within, and I was working for a client: I was filling a space which was already established, and that's journalism.

AF: But some people—some of your colleagues—would say that you shouldn't taint yourself with jazz and film music. That you've got to be pure.

RRB: Oh, yes, I know all about that. I think that's a very 1950s attitude. Indeed, when I started, there were quite a lot of noses in the air, and I think those people forgot that—who shall we say?—Britten, Walton, John Ireland, Vaughan Williams, Arnold Bax, Lord Berners: they all did movie music. It was a tradition in England. And in France, let's think about: Milhaud, Poulenc, Honegger . . .

AF: Auric.

RRB: Auric particularly. And that tradition is gone now, unfortunately. But I was part of a tradition. And so, there was a certain sniffy attitude when I started doing films, and it's very interesting that later on quite a lot of those people were hustling like mad to get movies, because they had to support themselves. I've sort of gone exactly the other way, in that those movies were a kind of investment for me. I mean, I get two pennies every time *Murder on the Orient Express* is shown. And when it's shown on television I get quite a lot more. And so if I wanted to take a year off and not write at all, I suppose I could. I'm not rich, but ever since I was 19 I've had an income from my music, and— listen—who could complain about that? Occasionally movies have been a nightmare to do. But I was exercising my craft. And there are few composers [who] can say that they always did that. But you're absolutely right, I have compartmentalised my musical ability and I get a certain sneaky pleasure out of that.

AF: You're saying that music is music—you're exercising your musical craft at all costs—but there's a sort of paradox there with the compartmentalisation, isn't there? Because, if I had to ask you which was your best music . . .

RRB: It's my classical, it's my concert music. That's what *I* think, but maybe you wouldn't. The classical music continues to be difficult to write, and it's challenging and it uses all my brain. That's all I can say. The movie music couldn't possibly use all your musical ability. And the jazz—the cabaret music—is something which if I didn't enjoy it, I would stop doing it.

AF: What music do you listen to?

RRB: Less and less. It's a perfectly good question. But I don't quite know how to answer it. There was a time when I was in love with the whole contemporary music scene; and in 1979, I left London and I went to live in New York, and I'm less and less interested in the contemporary music scene. Partly because it's so divorced from audiences, and I hated the fact that when my music was played it was so often played to the converted. You mentioned a piece called *Zodiac*. That was commissioned by the National Symphony in Washington and I was there for it, and I liked the piece and I went to all the performances, and one of the performances was for the Friday afternoon ladies' audience subscription series. And I knew they were all ready to hate it.

AF: Well, having twelve movements doesn't help, does it?

RRB: I think there were seventeen movements, with ritornellos and things. But it got them. And, in the weirdest way, I was much more anxious to convert all those ladies, than I was to impress the contemporary music circle. I don't give a damn about those people. I really don't. But I haven't answered your question.

AF: Do you keep up to date with contemporary music?

RRB: I don't know what that means. Really. What is 'up to date'?

AF: Well, I mean . . .

RRB: I'm not being cute.

AF: I know. Well, say, the latest Boulez piece: do you get along to listen to it; do you buy the disc?

RRB: Oh, yes, yes. I've talked to a number of musicians about that, about the fact that there aren't so many heroes nowadays. I mean the Boulez music which is important to me is the Boulez music that has always been important to me, which is his early music, as it happens. I was his student in the 50s and what he was writing then was amazing. I don't have so many heroes. I mean I will go and hear anything that Carter writes. I will hear anything that Dutilleux writes. There are a handful of friends of mine who I think are very good composers, notably Thea Musgrave, Peter Maxwell Davies (most of the time), Harry

Birtwistle, Nicholas Maw and Tristan Kueris. But I no longer have that hunger to hear everything that's new. This is partly to do with growing up. I'm so much more interested in the ideas behind Elliott [Carter]'s music than I am in actually listening to it. I was in New York and I was with John McCabe, who's a friend of mine, and we went to a rehearsal by Maxwell Davies' group—what were they called?

AF: The Fires [of London].

RRB: The Fires. At Symphony Space in New York. And they were doing Elliott's *Triple Duo*. I was listening to the rehearsal—and I was dying to hear that piece—and I said to John, all of a sudden, 'If I hear this kind of sound any more, I am going to go crazy.' I thought, I don't want to hear this sound any more; I'm familiar with this sound. The ideas behind Elliott's music could keep you in ideas of how to write music for the rest of your life. But I don't actually like the surface. I really care a lot about Harry [Birtwistle]'s music, although I don't understand why one note follows another.

AF: I find it unanalysable.

RRB: Completely. And you know, being a pupil of Boulez, and being very heavily influenced by late Webern at one time, I sort of expect to be able to take music apart, and look at it, and Harry's music makes no sense. He's one of the few composers—maybe Varèse. I never understood note one of Varèse.

AF: It still seems strange to me, in view of the diversity of your career, that you studied with Boulez.

RRB: I went to him because that's what I wanted to write like. And, in those days, you can't imagine how hard it was to get to hear that music. Even to see that music. We all used to go to Darmstadt. I used to hitchhike every year to Darmstadt, and Cornelius went, and a few other people, and we used to go to the library and copy out manuscripts by hand. I copied Stockhausen [piano pieces] 5, 7, 8, and some of 6, because they weren't published. But we had to have them. And that's kind of exciting. It was like an underground, you know? I remember sitting up with Cornelius, listening to Stuttgart radio, in the middle of the night—they had a program called *Nachtstudio*, where they used to play all the new pieces—and there was no way you could hear that new music in England at all. But the one thing Boulez taught me, I suppose, was *not* to want to write like that. Because at that age you assume things without questioning. It's a sort of teenage thing you do, and I used numbers and all that stuff, because Boulez did. That's where I was musically at that time—except I was also doing the movies—and there's a tea-chest full of my scores from those years in the house of a friend in London, and it's a sort of Pandora's Box. I can't bear to look at it; it's so long ago.

AF: That passion for the toughest of post-war serial music: it seems to have been very intense. Do you think there's a more relaxed attitude among younger composers today?

RRB: I don't teach any more, but when I was teaching, in the 1970s, I used to say to my students, 'Who do you really care about?' And they'd say, 'Oh, well, mmm. Lutoslawski's nice.' You know, there was no more than that. They were so passive. In the 50s, we were copying out manuscripts by hand and we were playing *Structures* on two upright pianos and we were listening to the radio in the middle of the night in *drastic need* to get to that music. And it was a very good time.

AF: You mentioned Cardew. And you said you were good buddies . . .

RRB: Great.

AF: How did you feel about the direction in which he went? The Maoist philosophy? The Scratch Orchestra? Those very simple pentatonic workers' songs?

RRB: Initially, we all went off in different directions. I mean, Sandy [Goehr] went to Messiaen, Max[well Davies] went to Petrassi, I went to Boulez, Cornelius went eventually to Stockhausen. And after about 1962–63, Cornelius and I couldn't talk to one other any more. Cornelius was extraordinarily musical, but he was completely blinkered. When we were both at the Royal Academy of Music together, and close friends, he was only interested in number theories, in an extremely complicated way, and that was food and drink to me at the time, so we had a lot to talk about. But the moment he went abroad and went to Stockhausen and helped him write *Carré*, he wasn't looking in my direction any more. He was not a highly articulate person, he could only talk about the things that were close to him. And it was sad, because we drifted apart. We used to see one another at the occasional party, and just sort of wave or say hello, but we couldn't talk to one another any more. And then he got into the whole Marxist thing, and I thought what he was doing was nonsense, I really did. And the Scratch Orchestra, and all that. He liked jazz, and he could play jazz, but he kind of despised the movie music I was doing. He thought it was selling out. He had every right to think that, but I wasn't. And then of course, he died. And it was terrible. But the Darmstadt years were something else, they really were.

AF: One thing I've wanted to ask you is about the whole postmodern, neo-romantic, minimalist axis . . .

RRB: I think the only thing that is important is whether something is new for you. Now, I did a third symphony, three years ago, which has been played a lot, and at one point in the last movement, which is slow, it comes to a C minor chord, and the C minor chord had nothing to do with George Rochberg, and had nothing to do with neo-romanticism; it was what [the piece] needed there. And I've been able to loosen up enough technically that I was able to do it without looking over my shoulder. It seemed the right thing to do at that time, and it went into a whole series of strange tonal chords that were sort of divorced from one another. And I was terribly proud of it because it was something I hadn't been able to do before. One of the things about the fact that I've covered so many different areas of music is that within my concert music I've always been very strict with myself. I don't use all kinds of eclectic things; I don't like that kind of music, really. But it was fascinating to find that I'd come to a place where that door was open to me. That I could find a C minor chord. But it was new for *me*, and that's the important thing.

AF: What do you think about minimalism? About Reich and Glass and Adams?

RRB: Reich, yes; Glass, no. Reich was doing it for quite a long time before Glass. John Adams I find very sympathetic—some of his pieces. I don't *care* very much any more. I really don't. I mean the good people will stay, and the little hangers-on—the little parasites—will disappear without a trace. I think as you grow older—I'm 53—you don't want things so badly. You don't feel you've got to see such-and-such a movie, you haven't got to have those kinds of clothes, you haven't got to have that person—you know, whatever it was that consumed you when you were 20. And now, it's not that I've lost interest, but I think, 'Oh yes, well that's interesting, that's what they're doing.' But this is what *I'm* doing, which is different. And I hope it's always something which is new, for me, and the only thing that frightens me is copying myself, starting to eat my own tail. You know what I mean? Sometimes, when you're feeling very barren, you start imitating pieces you wrote that worked. But I'm waiting for something new to come out of myself, and it won't come from outside. You know, if I suddenly hear a new romantic piece, that's not going to influence me. And Glass and Reich are worlds away from anything to do with me. It's not that I'm not interested, but it doesn't seem relevant to me.

AF: Do you go and listen much to performances of your music?

RRB: No. My music gets played quite a lot and I don't need to be there, because it's like old love letters being read out. You know you meant it and it was all you could do at the time, but . . . oh God! I like to read that they've been played and I hope people like them; I hope the *players* like them—that's who I'm writing for.

AF: You mentioned earlier that you don't teach any more. What approach did you take to teaching composition?

RRB: I'm ruthless with students about notation; about the practicalities of instruments. Because it is fiercely competitive now, and I've spent enough ghastly afternoons reading hundreds and hundreds of scores. And you open page one and it's illiterate and you close it again. That's all there is to it. Or it's written in ballpoint pen, in a spiral-bound notebook and you think, 'Oh, please!' I once taught a film music course at Dartington—two years running—and it was actually a thinly disguised course in the nuts and bolts of composition, and how you orchestrate and how you get things onto the page so players read them back correctly. And they had to copy their own parts. And—this is fascinating—I had one American student who had studied with Milton Babbitt, and I said, all right, if anybody fucks up, their music won't get played. And this boy had written a very fancy score and he thought that when there were bars of 5/8, 4/4 and 7/8, you just wrote three bars' rest.

AF: Three equal bars?

RRB: Gospel.

AF: Yes, I've had students like that . . .

RRB: But he'd been with *Babbitt*, for God's sake, he had a scholarship to Dartington, and he didn't know how to write an instrumental part that anyone could play from. That was what that class was about—I'm much more interested in that than in their musical souls. So I help them with it, I try and point them in the right direction, and sometimes I prescribe, like a doctor prescribes. I'll say: you ought to listen to Dallapiccola, or you ought to listen to *Dumbarton Oaks*, because it will help you. And that's the most a composer can do. What used to depress me so, when I was teaching a lot, was opening scores and it looked as though they'd never heard any music and they were never in love with somebody's music. You know it's like somebody who's never had a sex life that was worth anything—they've never been in love, they've never gone head-over-heels. I'd rather open a score and find it looks like Berio, than looks like . . . B flat major. Do you know what I mean? When I was 14 I wanted to write like Vaughan Williams and Peter Warlock. And then I wanted to write like Elisabeth Lutyens—because she was a huge influence on me—and Dallapiccola, and Boulez, and eventually you grow up. I was so in love with music that—I wouldn't steal, I was too bright for that—but I would let these joyful influences come in. And when I began to be sophisticated enough to know I couldn't do that, then I grew up. I mean Henze was a huge influence on me, but there's not one place in my music—I mean, please God!— where you could say, that's Henze.

AF: You mentioned Elisabeth Lutyens. She wrote some beautiful pieces.

RRB: She certainly did. And she was such an electric person when we were young. Malcolm [Williamson] and I were both heavily influenced by Liz. It was the technical thing which was so fascinating. You know: early 50s serial music—but with that lyrical quality. She was very, very important to me. I never studied with her. And she said I plagiarised her music, but she used to say terrible things about nearly everybody in the world. I really loved her . . . until when she was old. She was a horrible old woman: she was violently anti-semitic in the way that only the British aristocracy could be. 'Oh, your family should have gone to the gas ovens.' She said that to a young Jewish composer. Oh, yes. But she was a vital person in English music. In a funny way she had no technique at all. I mean she couldn't have written a fugue to save her life. But she had a way of just writing marvellous music; she was a natural. And all of us—I don't know about Harry—but Sandy and Max and Malcolm and I: we were all influenced by Liz. And a whole generation after us.

AF: In a sense she was before her time, wasn't she? Because she really belonged to a generation which should still have been writing English pastoral music.

RRB: Yes. I mean she was writing serial music in England before the war. She wrote much, much, much too fast. A lot of it was just a sort of stream of consciousness. She would work with the series and just have a stroke on the gong and then a few notes on the flute and it was magic; but it wasn't good. But *some* of her music is very good.

AF: One of her pieces I like very much is *And Suddenly It's Evening* . . .

RRB: I knew you were going to say that. It's a magic piece.

AF: I heard Gerald English sing it.

RRB: He sang in my first opera, it was called *The Ledge*.

AF: Would you write any more operas?

RRB: No. Never.

AF: Why?

RRB: It's something I went through.

AF: But why wouldn't you go back to it?

RRB: I never liked the opera house. I like voices and I like words but I never liked the opera house.

AF: Too many conventions?

RRB: Too many conventions. And I'm not the sort of composer who could envisage a new departure in that way. No. And I don't like opera singers very much.

AF: Have you ever tried to bridge the gap between jazz and your concert music?

RRB: No, no. I don't know how you can.[1]

AF: Do you think Gershwin succeeded?

RRB: Yes. I do. And who else?

AF: Milhaud?

RRB: No. Not Milhaud, not Stravinsky . . .

AF: Not Milhaud in *La création du monde*?

RRB: No. It's not a jazz piece. It's a piece which uses some of the mannerisms of jazz, which were very simple mannerisms in those days. So Stravinsky was able to do it in a number of pieces, like *Piano Rag Music*. And Milhaud did it in *La création du monde*. And a few American composers did it.

AF: What about Kurt Weill?

RRB: Kurt Weill was Kurt Weill and it's not really jazz. There's an enormous difference. I was in New Zealand recently, and I was lecturing to the National Association of Music Teachers and I was doing a course on the performance of contemporary music. And somebody played the Gershwin Preludes. And she thought, this is jazz, so she dotted all the rhythms, which made nonsense of the piece. I said, 'This is not jazz; it's a sort of salon version of jazz'.

AF: And yet it does say right at the top of that score: *Con licenza* . . .

RRB: That doesn't mean you distort all the rhythms. I mean how you play jazz is basically something that a classical musician couldn't do. People say to me, couldn't you notate what you play, when you play 'Sophisticated Lady'? No I couldn't. Apart from anything else, it's spontaneous; I can't remember a minute later what I've done. But also if you try to notate the way I phrase a tune—or any jazz musician phrases a tune—you get into such fearful complications of irrational rhythms and rhythms which go right across the pulse. You can't do it. Jazz is something else. It's not classical music.

---

1   In 1991 Bennett composed a concerto for jazz saxophonist Stan Getz, which does indeed 'cross over' between classical music and jazz.

AF: Who, for you, are the outstanding songwriters of the 20th century in that idiom, and why?

RRB: Gershwin. Harold Arlen. Cole Porter. Obvious names.

AF: Kern?

RRB: Kern. And then Jimmy van Heusen and others who are not names that people would recognise so quickly, although they'd know the songs. I'm trying to think what it is . . . You can take any of those composers' songs and you can treat them any way. Now with a lot of contemporary songs, there's only one way you can do them. But you can sing 'Embraceable You' and you can do a million things with the harmony, and you can rethink the phrasing of the words with the music, and pull it around rhythmically, and it will always be a major song whatever you do.

AF: There was one song tonight—I think it was 'How Long Has This Been Going On?': there was an extraordinary key change; I couldn't work out what was happening.

RRB: It might have been a mistake.

AF: Perhaps you weren't aware of it?

RRB: No, I am aware of it.

AF: Was it that song?

RRB: Yes. There is a sudden key change in that song. There's one point in that song—just the last stanza of all—I suddenly go sideways into a different key. And I've got another thing that I do, which is suddenly to change key downwards. I do a Jerome Kern song called 'The Folks Who Live On the Hill' and there's a line: 'And when the kids grow up and leave us . . .' and I change down there. Because I think harmony is emotion in those tunes. That's why Andrew Lloyd Webber gives me such horrors, because there is no emotion in that harmony. Key changes I find absolutely electric and I do different things every night; I will always try and rethink the harmony as I go along. And how do you teach somebody to do that? I don't know.

Adelaide, March 1990

Roger Smalley

Making an impact

Roger Smalley

Like me, Roger Smalley is an English expatriate with an Australian passport. The following conversation took place in my kitchen on one of his visits to Sydney from Western Australia, where he lives.

AF: Why do you think there has been such an extraordinary explosion of musical styles in the 20th century? Do we know any longer what terms such as 'modern' or 'avant-garde' mean?

RS: Well, it's difficult to say exactly what's caused it—it must be different from composer to composer. In Mozart, say, or Brahms, there's a relatively small stylistic evolution, but what has happened now is that there are composers in whose works there's a definite break between a first style and a second style, or maybe even a third style. But this also happened back in the 1950s amongst composers who had started as tonal composers and then underwent some form of conversion, and rejected or disowned or even burned all their early tonal efforts, pronouncing themselves to be serial composers. My generation started off from that point; we were serialists from the word go. The sort of music that was attractive to me to begin with—not because it was serial but because it was what I liked—was Webern and late Stravinsky . . . I can remember among the first works of new music that I was really struck by were Stravinsky's *Movements* and *Agon*—which is still my favourite of those late pieces. And with Webern, it was the String Quartet and the piano variations, which I used to play. I wasn't attracted by their technical sophistication, because I didn't know how they'd been composed. All I had to go on were the little articles in *Tempo*, which would have a few musical illustrations with numbers written over them. So I was never really a serial composer in the Webernian sense—I've hardly ever written a piece which was based on a twelve-tone row—and one of the reasons for that was that I didn't really know how they manipulated it all. I knew a lot of new music—the Webern, the Stravinsky, some Stockhausen, Berio's *Circles* and so on—because I heard it at the BBC Invitation Concerts when I was a student. And of course the ideal thing would have been to go to one's next compo-

216

sition lesson at the Royal College of Music with a score of *Circles* and say to one's teacher, 'Here, explain to me how this is put together'. But the point was that there was nobody there who could do it.

AF: Who were you studying with?

RS: Well, with Peter Racine Fricker. The alternatives would have been Herbert Howells, Gordon Jacobs or Philip Cannon. I went to Fricker because I knew he had at least composed some twelve-tone music. But he was as up in the air as I was about all this new stuff. So I had to try to find somebody else.

AF: So you went to Sandy Goehr.

RS: Yes, but he didn't say anything about serialism. He was teaching evening classes at Morley College which were for all comers, and included some budding composers. We learned an awful lot about musical structure. Sandy taught in the Schoenberg manner, which is to say you analyse the classics, and then if you've got anything original to say it will come out. We analysed Bach chorale preludes; Mozart, Haydn and Beethoven symphony movements; the *Diabelli* Variations. The one serial piece that we looked at in detail was the Schoenberg Variations for Orchestra, but Sandy's approach to that was to look at it without ever referring to the fact that it was a twelve-tone piece. You can look at all the musical techniques—they're quite classical, they're just applied to a more chromatic idiom—but you don't have to get into the serial procedures. I think Sandy felt that it was so easy to get seduced by the idea of putting numbers all over the score, and to imagine that this explained something about the music.

AF: It tells you where the pitches come from.

RS: Yes, but that's about all. The first composer whose music I understood the inner workings of was Peter Maxwell Davies. I was very impressed by that music—the *early* Peter Maxwell Davies.

AF: You mean works like *Prolation* and so forth?

RS: Not as early as that. I've never actually, to this day, heard that piece . . . No, the Monteverdi-based works like the *Sinfonia*, the String Quartet, the cantata . . . what's that cantata?

AF: *Leopardi Fragments?*

RS: Yes—which is a beautiful piece. I was attracted to those pieces because of their very telling, economical musical language, in which everything seemed to be related to everything else. Anyway, his was the first music that I got a technical grasp of. My first pieces which were successful and played a bit were very much based on Max's *cantus firmus* principles. And that went on for quite a while until about 1969 when I had one of those switches we were talking about earlier—from a Max Davies-influenced style to a much more Stockhausen-influenced style.

AF: This really is a very major shift, isn't it, from music based on a *cantus firmus* to 'moment' form. In a sense they're diametrically opposed: there is a continuity, a flow associated with the use of a *cantus*.

RS: Yes. There were various thoughts going through my mind at the time. On the one hand, I had begun to feel that Max's music was demanding too much prior knowledge on the part of the listener. Particularly when you get to works like *Vesalii icones* and so on: the complexity of manipulation of this material, with the stylistic references and the use of plainsongs which, if you could even recognise what they were, you also had to know what the texts were, and these were some kind of ironic commentary on another text . . . I began to feel this was demanding too much input from the audience. On the other hand, what attracted me more than anything to Stockhausen was the way he was able to build up pieces from a consideration of the most basic elements, related to the physical nature of sound. I was very impressed by Stockhausen's pronouncements that every piece must be unique; every ensemble must be specifically created for one piece and never used again. I certainly don't believe that now, but I did then.

AF: Does *Accord* mark the end of this period of Stockhausen's direct influence?

RS: *Accord* comes in 1975, so you could say that the heavily Stockhausen-influenced period ran from the late 60s to the mid 70s. And it coincided with the existence of Intermodulation.

AF: Intermodulation was an ensemble of four players, working largely in the area of improvised or semi-improvised music with electronics . . .

RS: Yes, we were playing the text pieces of Stockhausen and the *Plus-Minus* pieces. And, of course, a lot of the pieces that I wrote during that period were for Intermodulation, so much so that it's almost impossible to perform them any longer. When I first came to Australia, I remember trying to get together with other interested students and composers to do some of the Stockhausen text pieces. I pretty quickly realised that, if you hadn't got the same kind of musical background that I had, and all the other members of Intermodulation had, you really couldn't do them satisfactorily. They're not free improvisation pieces in which any stylistic approach will do, they only work success-fully when they're performed within a stylistic context set by Stockhausen's written-down pieces, and one has to know them. As soon as I was playing with people who weren't familiar with this background, it just didn't work. So I could see that I wasn't going to be able to continue doing that sort of thing; I also had this five-year output of pieces which nobody could perform. And I was suddenly in Perth, and not in London, Berlin, Cologne or anywhere like that. If I was going to write something which was going to mean anything to an Australian public, I obviously couldn't do this sort of music. And I did increasingly feel that I wanted to communicate. So from 1976, when I finally settled in Australia, I tried all kinds of different approaches. I wrote a music–theatre work, *William Derrincourt* [1978], which was very important for me because, as you know, it's based on the autobiography of an ex-convict and I had to deal with real dramatic situations: there a dance scene, there are parades, there's the singing of the national anthem. This had a very liberating effect on me, because it forced me to do all kinds of stylistic things which I would never have done before, and it broadened my musical palette.

AF: For someone with your background and with the reputation you'd acquired in Europe, Perth was a pretty extreme choice, wasn't it? To move to Perth was to go as far away as you could get from the source of that reputation.

RS: But you see I felt that as long as I remained in Europe it would be very difficult to escape the spectre of Stockhausen, as it were. I didn't make any conscious choice to come to Australia or to Perth, it was an accident. But if I hadn't liked it or felt that it was stimulating, then I wouldn't have stayed. So it was a happy accident. But there had been a lot of dissatisfaction, and the piece you mentioned earlier, *Accord*, which I wrote between my first, brief visit to Perth in 1974 and my return in '76, is the key work. I almost consider it to be my opus 1, rather like Busoni, who wrote lots and lots of pieces until his mid-30s when he composed the second violin sonata and the Piano Concerto, and then he said, 'Well, this is where it really starts'. In a sense *Accord*, for me, is where it really starts; everything I've done since then relates back to that piece in some way or another.

AF: So everything else is sort of like *Das Rheingold*, and *The Ring* proper starts with *Accord* . . .

RS: Well, everything else may be *Rienzi* . . . But, you know, the thing about *Accord* is that it seemed to solve the harmonic problem. The reason I never wrote twelve-tone music was that, with Schoenberg, the harmonic aspect was so uncontrolled. Of course I liked Webern more because there it was controlled.

AF: Especially in the late works.

RS: Yes, but only by dint of restricting everything to so few intervals and such small cells is it possible to do that. I suppose you could say Babbitt does it as well. In *Accord* I thought of the basic material vertically; it's basically one chord—'a chord'—and several variants of it, and then several sub-chords which are built up on the intervals of the main chord. The linear aspect of the music is a projection of the vertical, rather than writing a linear music which happens to give rise to vertical results. Again, another aspect of twelve-tone music that I didn't like was simply its twelve-tone-ness: this continual recycling of all twelve tones made it very difficult to focus the listener's ear on any one pitch or interval. So I began to develop modes which concentrated on different intervals so that each part of the piece could have a distinct harmonic character. These techniques have remained ever since; I've expanded them a great deal, but in an unsystematic way.

AF: Do you start a piece by sketching ideas? Do you sit at the piano?

RS: Well, I never really sit at the piano . . . What do I do . . . ? I very often start from the number and nature of the instruments. For instance, the quintet [*Poles Apart*; 1992] which I'm writing for the Australia Ensemble, and which I thought of, at first, as being in four movements, but now seems to want to be in three—I thought a lot about the instruments. The violin and the flute are high, and the cello and the bass clarinet are low, and the viola is in the middle. So that immediately gives you some kind of basis on which to evolve a form: you'll have one duo playing one kind of material, and the other duo playing another kind, and the viola mediating between them. Then I think of an overall form which is often related to the idea of the transformation of one kind of musical material into another. In *Echo III* [1978], the idea is to transform staccato material into legato material. I often use double forms, which I liken to Haydn's double variation form, where I constantly juxtapose two streams of development going in different directions. I like to expose the limits at the very beginning of a piece, so in *Echo III* you have the staccato material first and then you have extremely sustained material immediately following it. Or in *Strung Out* [for thirteen solo strings; 1988] you have the juxtaposition of the first idea—which is a single held note and has no tempo at all in essence—and then this very fast, active section. Gradually the characters begin to exchange and there's the pizzicato passage in the middle of the piece where these materials meet. And then it all comes full circle: in *Strung Out* the last note is the first note and it could all go round again. So I think very much of those kinds of formal conceptions, related to the instrumental possibilities of the ensemble being used.

AF: And this includes their sonic possibilities?

RS: Yes. I can't orchestrate like Boulez, you know, with this extremely elaborate, constantly changing doubling of many different types of instruments; I tend to think in primary colours, of blocks of sonority. This is very clear in my piano concerto [1985], where—

although it became more elaborate in the long run—I initially thought the first movement would be mainly brass, the second mainly woodwind, the third mainly strings, and the fourth everything together. It turned out to be much more complicated than that, but even so you have, at the beginning of the piece, the piano with the timpani, then the tuba, the trombones, the horns, the trumpets. So this is all . . .

AF: . . . like *The Young Person's Guide to the Orchestra!*

RS: Yes, except in retrograde. It happens in the new piece, as well [*Diptych: homage to Brian Blanchflower*; 1991]. It's thinking of the orchestra as blocks of primary colours, which you can superimpose to produce secondary mixtures, as it were. Nowadays there's a group of composers who are making their music more and more complex; I'm interested in making mine simpler. There's some confusion, I think, in the minds of composers of the 'new complexity' persuasion that somehow the sheer complexity of the music on the page, and the instrumental dexterity required, means that the music is going to have a complex effect in performance. Equally, music which looks simple on the page may produce a very, very complex response in the listener. And the best example I can think of for that is the slow piano solo in my piano concerto, which people have said reminds them of everything from Chopin's E minor prelude, to the *Arioso* from Beethoven's opus 110. That's one of the simplest bits of music I've ever written, and yet its effect on people who hear it is extraordinarily diverse and complex, because it awakens all kinds of half memories of music of the past.

AF: Have you learned anything from minimalism?

RS: I like some minimal music. But I like it more the more complex it is. So obviously I'm not a minimalist. I certainly don't find it so interesting that I would want to do it; I mean, I find the thought of composing and writing out the score of a piece like Reich's *The Desert Music* to be unimaginably tedious. I want my music to be more changeable than that.

AF: What about the Eastern European composers, such as Górecki?

RS: It's essentially a spiritually focused form of minimalism and I haven't got that in me. I appreciate what they're doing; again, it doesn't interest me to write minims all day. Although since I've begun to conduct more, I've learned a healthy respect for the minim! No, I like a greater diversity of material and more formal ambiguity in my own music. As a composer, my strengths are more in the way of what I do with the material than in the invention of the material, and to be a minimalist it has to be the other way around; you have to have some very striking initial invention to arrest the ear of the listener, because if you can't do that at the beginning, you sure as hell aren't going to be able to do it later in the piece. So my material is usually fairly basic; it's what I do with it that makes it interesting. Although I'm trying to start pieces with more and more memorable ideas.

AF: Well, the piano concerto certainly has that. Isn't there even an instruction to the soloist at the beginning of that score to take the audience by surprise?

RS: Yes, there is. I imagined myself sitting in the audience. You know, the soloist walks on and sits down, and I was thinking, 'What can happen here that's not happened in any other piano concerto?' And I had the idea that the pianist plays this whacking great chord and then nothing happens. Then he plays it again. And just as you think he's going to play it a third time, another chord suddenly comes from the orchestra.

AF: You've played your concerto a number of times and you're doing more and more conducting. What's your attitude to interpretation? Do you ever take liberties with your own music in performance?

RS: I do in the piano concerto. I tend to sacrifice accuracy to impact.

AF: How do you feel about others doing that?

RS: I was thinking about it this morning at the rehearsal [of *Diptych*, with Gunther Schuller conducting the Sydney Symphony Orchestra]. When Schuller had played through the piece I was wondering what I should say about it. I suppose I might have said certain things about the interpretation, like: 'It's immensely clear and well-balanced, but it could be more exciting; you could let it rip more, even at the risk of compromising the accuracy'. But I didn't actually say any of this, because I thought that this guy is obviously a very fine musician, this is the way he sees it, and his interpretation does no violence to the music. The more you restrict the scope of the performer—if you write fourteen in the time of fifteen, at a tempo of semiquaver equals 94.5, and if it's important that these directions be observed—then you're not leaving the performer very much latitude. It seems to me to be more rewarding to leave the performer a bit of room to move.

Sydney, May 1992

Poul Ruders

Hanky-panky in Tooting Bec

Poul Ruders

Tooting Bec Hospital in South London is one of those imposing Victorian lunatic asylums—all red brick and turrets. As I walk its long driveway looking for the ward Poul Ruders lives in, I have no idea whether he is a patient, a doctor, an orderly, or a cleaner—I had been too embarrassed to ask him.

I climb to the third floor, where I am confronted by double doors, inscrutably institutional with their windows of thick frosted glass and criss-crossed wire reinforcement. I ring the bell. I knock. Finally, I shout. Nobody comes. Beyond the glass, I can dimly make out a long, dark corridor that seems to lead to a larger, lighter area (presumably the ward). The place is deserted.

I see what's happening. I have never knowingly encountered the Danish sense of humour before, but obviously it delights in practical jokes: Ruders hates to talk about his music, so when anyone asks for an interview he sends them to Tooting Bec mental hospital.

I descend the stairs to the ward below. This one is buzzing with administrative activity, and I approach a woman behind a typewriter.

'I'm supposed to interview someone in the ward upstairs,' I risk.

'Are you sure? There aren't any interview rooms upstairs,' the woman replies, apparently believing me to be a psychiatrist. (Just wait till I speak to his publisher!)

'He's a composer,' I continue, well aware that under the circumstances this sounds like 'He's Napoleon Bonaparte' or 'He's an armadillo'.

'Oh, the Swedish gentleman.' (So he *does* live here!)

'Well, Danish actually.'

'Yes. Was he expecting you?'

'About 20 minutes ago. I've been ringing and knocking, but there's no one up there.'

'That's not like him. I'll ring security and check if he's been seen going out.' He has. (*Is* he a patient?)

I ring Ruders' publisher and explain the situation.

'And he's not there? Well, that's not like him.'

224

I decide to wait it out, and sit in the garden outside his ward, where I am approached by a constant stream of people asking me for cigarettes, which I don't have. It takes some of them only five minutes to forget this and ask again.

An hour has passed and I climb the stairs to the third floor once more. This time the door is opened in response to my banging. It is not the composer.

'I'm here to interview Poul Ruders,' I tell the man.

'I'll see if he's in,' he replies, knocking on another door. There is no response.

'And he was expecting you? This isn't at all like him.'

I write the composer a note, saying that I'm sorry to have missed him but can wait no longer, and I begin the long walk back to the hospital's wrought iron gates. As I near them, the composer strides into view. He sees me, stops in his tracks and claps one hand to his forehead, whilst the other begins foraging in his pocket. Out comes a diary, pages are riffled, he slaps his forehead once more then rushes forward with a handshake and profuse apologies (which punctuate our conversation for the next hour).

'I don't suppose you'd believe me if I told you this is most unlike me,' he says.

Poul Ruders is not mentally ill. Eight months ago, when he decided to live in London, the pianist Rolf Hind found for him in Tooting Bec Hospital a tiny flat for which the composer pays a peppercorn rent. We retire to it and Ruders percolates some coffee as we talk about his expatriate status.

'Not that I'm not being extremely pampered in Denmark with performances of my music, but I've always had this urge to try and live abroad. I'm 43, I'm no spring chicken any more, and last year it seemed appropriate to give it a try. My music is being extremely well received in this country—to put it mildly—I have more friends in the trade here than I have back home, and I've always liked London a lot, so it was a quite natural jump to make. It's impossible to pursue a career out of Denmark. There is something in the Danish national character—Hans Christian Andersen wrote about it, so did Holberg—a tendency to drag down whoever wants to poke his or her nose too much forth. It's like jogging in a quagmire: the more you run, the more you will be pulled down in a swamp of laziness and mediocrity. I'm being very hard now, but it is what I think is the truth. That's a major reason that I'm here. I've fled to an active, open-minded city.'

I mention that one of the reasons I now live in Sydney is that London, to me, had seemed anything but open-minded, and we agree that possibly another country's grass seems a brighter green.

Poul Ruder's music is remarkable for its almost complete lack of stylistic homogeneity. It is almost as though each piece is the work of a different composer. I wondered whether his pieces were, in a sense, *about* musical style.

'Yes. It's true. My training as a composer is virtually non-existent. I mean stylistically—I had a very good formal conservatory training in orchestration, for which I'm very grateful, because the symphony orchestra is my main medium. But stylistically I have been groping in the dark for many years. My period of apprenticeship has been very long indeed. *Four Compositions* [1980] is my second opus one, so to speak; it's the piece where one can probably start to see the contour, the profile of whoever I am.

'I recently had a series of pieces performed at the Platform 2 Festival here in London, and I had printed in the program book my so-called "Second Confession"—which implies, of course, that there must have been a previous one. In my "First Confession", which I wrote in Denmark for a festival almost devoted to my music, I confessed to not believing in modernism or in music history proceeding in one uninter-rupted stretch, where each day is an improvement on the preceding one. In the "Second Confession" I tackled the problem that some people have with my music, which is that I seem to have—to paraphrase Monteverdi—a first and second practice. Actually it's probably more like a first, second and third practice. For instance, the second violin concerto [1992], which is a modern-day fin de siècle piece of romantic music, was written immediately after *The Second Nightshade* [1991] for the Scottish Chamber Orchestra. Now even I, who wrote those pieces, readily admit that it is almost as though they were written by two separate composers. But it's not deliberately so—I'm not manipulative, I don't sit down and coldly calculate ways of baffling my audience—it's entirely dependent on what I write for.

'A violin concerto, in my mind, almost calls for tunes and a transparent symphonic background; the type of music is almost predes-tined to be what I guess would today be called "romantic", but what I would prefer to call "new intensity". *The Second Nightshade* is written for a Haydn-sized orchestra with trombones and is an instrumentally experimental piece; it's my first thoroughly composed quarter-tone piece, with all sorts of hanky-panky going on in the various instrumen-tal parts. It's much more a clenched fist of sound. But, if I try to step back and look at myself, I would say that I don't know of any other composer who is so difficult to pin down.'

Neither is it only between pieces that Ruders' character appears to change. Frequently even within one piece there is considerable contrast. This may be a contrast of movements, as in *The Second Nightshade*, whose first movement's quarter-tone 'hanky-panky' is followed by a chorale consisting entirely of what Ruders calls 'blatantly tonal' first inversion minor triads. But also, even within the movements them-selves, there are extremely sudden shifts of texture, dynamic or tempo.

'Yes, I have heard that I am a composer of extremes. And it's true, looking at the music from the outside. But, at the moment, I am quite cautious to limit the occurrences of extremes. That piece beside you on my writing desk is what I would call a piece of monomania. It's called *Gong* and was commissioned by the Danish National Symphony Orchestra for its European and American tour next year. One of Carl Nielsen's smaller orchestral pieces is his *Helios* overture inspired by a visit to Greece, and it's about the sun's journey from sunrise to sunset. Although it has nothing whatever to do with Nielsen, *Gong* is a sort of second *Helios* overture. In a span of sixteen or seventeen minutes I am trying to describe the history of the sun, from the initial explosion to the white dwarf ending, about 500 million years from now.

'It's called *Gong* because science has revealed that the sun reverberates like a gong in five different tempi. I talked about monomania, well this piece is about 47 huge chords being slowly heated up into a dance, and then heated up even more and I melt the music. And what you're looking at now, on page 67, we are approaching the ultimate heat—fewer and fewer intervals, less and less rhythm—it's getting really hot out there! So it's a piece of monomania with virtually no contrast—so again I'm contradicting myself.'

I asked Ruders whether he considered it an advantage or a disadvantage that it was so difficult to label his music.

'We live in an era of "ism"-mania. Some of my favourite pieces of the last 20 years have been minimal pieces. But minimalism at its worst—and I won't mention any names—tends to create a cult, because it is so easily pin-downable by people who are not too secure in themselves: it's easy to identify with; it's easy to be for or against. Whereas with a composer or a writer who is constantly surprising—a writer like Anthony Burgess—you never know what you're going to get next. So I follow that artistic avenue more or less voluntarily. And, yes, to me it is an advantage.'

The one label for which Poul Ruders is leaving himself wide open is, of course, 'post-modern', particularly since his music seems to refer so frequently to a variety of recognisable styles. Did he feel he was in any sense a post-modernist?

'I guess I am, but I've always hated that expression. The so-called post-modern era has become a comfort blanket for amateurs, because they think that anything goes. But it doesn't. Stylistic diversity is fine and, at times, even extremely convincing, but it still has to be composed. Composition actually means "putting together", and in this day and age, when we can legitimately draw on the history of music, law and order really has to prevail—you have to have an extremely solid scaffolding to hold the fragments of this and that together. But if I have to put a label on my music, then I would prefer to call it, with tongue in cheek, "new rage" music.'

If Ruders is reluctant to name the names of those minimalist composers whose music he finds boring, I wonder whether he might care to nominate those composers whose work he admires.

'Well, we spoke about minimalism, and I would say that what Louis Andriessen did in the 1970s was, quite simply, the best minimalism ever. It's an enigma to me that he is not as feverishly popular as Reich or Glass, but it's probably far too dangerous music to be popular. In this country, Harrison Birtwistle—it's no secret—is a major figure and strangely minimalist in his own way, with the limited material of pieces like *Secret Theatre* and *Carmen arcadiae mechanicae perpetuum*. I think what makes it strong music is that it combines intensity and economy. It's not particularly beautiful music; at times it's even ugly, but it's an attractive ugliness—and there's no hanky-panky.

'On the romantic side, so to speak, Sofia Gubaidulina has done at least two pieces that I think are extremely strong. You can't listen to the violin concerto *Offertorium* without being moved; you'd be a terrible stick-in-the-mud if you didn't allow yourself that. In America obviously Nancarrow is a major genius, although his music doesn't mean anything to me personally.'

Suddenly Ruders' voice turns to a whisper, as though he doesn't want my microphone to pick up what he is about to say.

'Schnittke, I think, is writing himself into a catastrophe; it has become almost pathetic. Unfortunately. Now, there's a bit of the negative side. Perhaps that should be off the record. I leave it up you to you. No—I stand by it. It is terrible, quite simply. And it could be so good.'

We return once more to the topic of 'ism'-mania which Ruders objects to so strongly. He says that he is very tired of music being 'talked to death' and lays the blame for this with 'the army of academic middle-men emerging from the woodwork', who, he maintains have greatly harmed the reputation of modern music. But, I ask him, perhaps a little defensively, is it not important to talk about contemporary music in an attempt to clarify what is going on, especially when it has the reputation of being obscure and impenetrable? Surely, for instance, he must have experienced that most common of reactions to one's music— the audience member who apologises for not having understood it?

'Oh, you're absolutely right. We always hear this. They are always saying "I liked your piece, but I didn't understand it". Where do they get this idea from that they ought to understand it? Music and books and paintings are primarily about an emotional impact; they have to move something inside us. If you understand it, it's an advantage—but only if you understand it in the right way. And here, of course, we come to the concept of analysis. I would say that wrong analysis is a harness against being moved, and we both know that in this trade many people, including composers, are scared stiff of being moved, of being emotionally punched about. The *right* sort of analysis enhances the emotional experience.'

Walking back again to the gates it strikes me as rather ironic that a composer who admits to a split musical personality should dwell in Tooting Bec Hospital. It also strikes me that the 'academic middle-men' Ruders disparages might consider that his sort of 'hanky-panky' is far better kept behind its doors.

London, July 1992

Martin Wesley-Smith

Dropping out

Martin Wesley-Smith

As our conversation nears the end of its third hour, and I make a rather ostentatious show of turning over yet another cassette, Martin Wesley-Smith apologises: 'I'm sorry, but no one ever asks me to talk about my music.'

Behind this artless admission lies the simple truth of the matter regarding Wesley-Smith's music. Many of his colleagues refuse to take it seriously; for his part, the composer is not so sure he cares.

We are in my kitchen a few days after the CD launch of Wesley-Smith's musical *Boojum!*, written in collaboration with his twin brother Peter. The recording marks the end of one of the most drawn-out sagas in Australian music—*Boojum!* occupied its creators for thirteen years. I asked how it all began.

'Peter and I had been to see Sondheim's *Sweeney Todd* on Broadway and I turned to him at the end of the show and said, "We're going to write a musical". *Sweeney Todd* was an attempt to write a serious Broadway musical, and I wanted to do something similar. We worked on it independently for about four years—I just had a folder marked "The Musical", although we'd already decided that it should be something to do with "The Hunting of the Snark". My marriage broke up and I needed to get into something as a cathartic experience, so I took myself off to Hong Kong, where Peter lives, and put my bulging folder together with Peter's bulging folder and we nutted out a basic approach.'

The actual composition of *Boojum!* occupied Wesley-Smith for most of 1985 and the work was presented at the Adelaide Festival in March 1986 in a production which the composer regards as 'a disaster'. The piece was revised and performed again in Brisbane and Sydney, and then further revised for the recording.

'Over thirteen years it's been the main preoccupation of my life and now it's on CD there's a fantastic sense of release—although it's still going on—there's a production of it in America next year.'

Part of the reason for the sniffy attitudes of some of Wesley-Smith's colleagues is that *Boojum!*, which includes musical styles ranging from blues to barbershop to Victorian drawing-room ballads, is an avowedly popular work. There is, after all, little point in writing a 'Broadway musical' that does not strive to be popular. But this creates its own problems for Wesley-Smith—problems seldom experienced by the sniffy colleagues.

'You can't just write something like *Boojum!*, put it on and then take refuge in the fact that it's a piece of art music, because it's not. If it doesn't work with a general audience, there's something wrong.'

If *Boojum!* was an obsession, it was also a summing up, in many ways, of an earlier obsession. Like the American composer David Del Tredici, Wesley-Smith has long been drawn to composing works based on the writings of Lewis Carroll.

'The first one was in 1974, a piece called *Doublets*, based on one of his word games—I wrote several *Doublets*. An audio-visual piece called *Dodgson's Dream* [1979] got me into a frame of mind where I wanted to explore lots of other things to do with Carroll, and then *Boojum!* came along. In getting ready to write the show, I did *Snark Hunting* and *White Knight and Beaver* [both 1984] to try out some of the ideas in a smaller form.'

Can Wesley-Smith explain the attraction of Lewis Carroll?

'I was never terribly interested in Carroll when I was a kid, in fact I remember finding *Alice's Adventures in Wonderland* quite frightening. The appeal came really from an intellectual interest in his word games and puzzles. But there was also an interest in Carroll himself: the paradox of this 19th century English clergyman—a boring and uninspired teacher and a stern moralist—who became the finest writer of nonsense, certainly in English and possibly in any language; his fascination with little girls and his penchant for photographing them naked; his ability to conjure up pure nonsense out of his mind, which today is seen to have uncanny connections with certain aspects of quantum theory. He's such a rich subject!

'I was taught to respect politicians from an early age and as I got older I realised that a lot of what they said was nonsense. This came clearly into focus during the Vietnam war, when some American general said the only way we could save a particular village was to destroy it. So I became fascinated by the connection between sense and nonsense, and Lewis Carroll sums it up better than anybody.'

There is a marked difference between Wesley-Smith's treatment of his Carrollian subjects and that of Del Tredici. In 1990, at Musica Nova in Brisbane, both composers were present and their works performed side by side. Does Wesley-Smith empathise with Del Tredici's approach?

'His music, to me, doesn't seem to have any relation to Lewis Carroll—it could be about anything, it's just that he happens to give his pieces *Alice* titles. I don't think he has any real depth of understanding about Carroll—he admitted as much to me. On a symposium at Musica Nova which Richard Mills was chairing, Del Tredici said that he got into Carroll because of a curiosity as to whether Carroll had fucked his little girlfriends or not, and his interest hadn't developed much past that point. It's certainly been an astute career move for him.'

In Wesley-Smith's own Carroll pieces the precise connections between the music and the writer stem, in the first place, from the collection of musical boxes which Carroll kept to entertain his young companions. A favourite trick of Carroll's was to have the clockwork devices play their nursery rhyme tunes backwards or upside down, and sometimes to play two of the musical boxes simultaneously. Wesley-Smith began to attempt to recreate the musical sounds that might have emanated from Carroll's own drawing-room. But this was only the start.

'In *Pat-A-Cake* [1980] I asked myself: "If Lewis Carroll were a composer (which he wasn't) and a trombone player (which he wasn't) and if he had a Fairlight CMI (which he didn't), what kind of music would he produce?" I took that particular song, "Pat-a-cake, pat-a-cake, baker's man"—which is a very Carrollian tune, because it already contains inversions and retrogrades, and also the words have some connections with "The Hunting of the Snark"—and tried to get into his head and explore some of the ideas in his puzzles and his writings. As far as I can be objective—which I can't [be] at all—I feel that I've got a musical picture which expresses a lot about Lewis Carroll himself. But I may be up myself totally.'

As might be expected from his views on the relationship of politicians to nonsense, Wesley-Smith is a supporter of political causes, none more so than the plight of East Timor since the Indonesian annexation in 1975. This has been an inspirational subject for his music almost as recurrent as Lewis Carroll.

'It wasn't that I was looking for a cause; this one insinuated itself and I've continued ever since. I did an audio-visual piece called *Kdadalak (For the Children of Timor)* [1977]. I was good friends with an English photo-journalist who was covering East Timor and got out on the last plane to leave before the invasion. She had these very strong black and white photographs and they became a part of my piece. Through this piece I got to meet a lot of Timorese people. When Bob Hawke became prime minister, I wrote another audio-visual piece, called VENCEREMOS! [1984]: this one was really a cry of outrage against the hypocrisy of an Australian prime minister who was elected on one platform, then changed his mind and sold out the people of Timor.'

Wesley-Smith's commitment to the Timorese cause continues in such works as *Balibo* [1992; for flute and tape] and the theatre piece *Quito* which deals with the suicide of a schizophrenic Timorese man whom the Wesley-Smith brothers had met in Darwin.

'He was a songwriter and a guitar player—he wasn't terribly good, but it was personal stuff. So I got caught up in this bloke's life and couldn't stop myself from trying to do something with his music. At about the time he developed schizophrenia he had heard that his sister's two children had died of starvation in Timor—she was on the run from the Indonesians. Schizophrenia is often triggered by a traumatic event, and although I can't say whether the event triggered the schizophrenia in this case, the parallel is strong dramatically.'

It seems at first a little incongruous that, besides writing multi-media political works and Lewis Carroll pieces, Wesley-Smith should also be one of Australia's leading exponents of computer music. But the composer's interests have always been as broad as his early musical training was unconventional.

'I was never schooled in a deep love and appreciation of classical music: my father had attempted to inculcate this in me, but I fiercely resisted it and went towards jazz and popular music. He would put on a record of a Mendelssohn concerto and he'd point out the French horn line and say, "Here they come, here they come!" and then he would sigh deeply as this wonderful melody emerged. I was bored shitless. And he used to say, "But all this jazz just sounds the same", and I couldn't understand what on earth he was talking about. The other day I found myself saying exactly the same thing to my son about rap music.

'At university I always felt like a country cousin. I was playing in a jazz band by night and studying Webern during the day. At one point I delivered a paper on Webern's opus 9, and I'd been to bed at three o'clock that morning, and I was taken aside and told that I had to choose between Webern and the banjo. Well, I couldn't possibly have given up playing in the band, because it was teaching me so much about music, it was helping me pay my way through university and, apart from anything else, it was my sole source of getting laid.'

Martin Wesley-Smith's place in the contemporary music scene is singular to say the least. On programs of new music his work invariably stands apart, whether it is distinguished by the sophisticated use of technology, the impassioned political messages of his Timorese works or the appearance of upside-down nursery rhymes. In so far as it is still possible to perceive a mainstream of contemporary music, one could be forgiven for thinking that Wesley-Smith has dropped out of it. Does the composer himself feel that his music fits into the general milieu of contemporary composition?

'Well, largely, it doesn't at all. And that used to worry me; but it doesn't now.'

Sydney, October 1992

Sir Michael Tippett

Pastel pumps

Sir Michael Tippett

Sir Michael Tippett wanted my red sneakers. These were to add to his collection of sneakers, which, when I spoke with him, were neatly lined up beneath the window of his room at the Brisbane Hilton. They made an impressive collection; a variety of largely pastel shades, some with spots.

'Would you like a hat?' Sir Michael inquired. Sensing that a swap was being proposed, I couldn't imagine that a hat would quite compensate for something on my feet once I was back on the streets. 'There's one over there,' he continued, indicating a mortar-board in mint condition, 'they gave it to me this time.'

Sir Michael was in Australia for two events: the Brisbane Tippett Festival and the Festival of Perth, where he was guest of honour and where the University of Western Australia granted him an honorary doctorate. By now he must have more doctorates than sneakers.

The mortar-board and a brightly coloured doctoral gown were presented to the composer after the ceremony and now constituted a serious luggage problem as he continued his latest world trip. 'It was very kind of them, but I don't know what to do with the things.'

Sir Michael Tippett is one of the most respected and frequently played composers alive. He is a committed pacifist who was imprisoned in Wormwood Scrubs as a conscientious objector during the second world war; now, besides his knighthood, he is a Companion of Honour and has the Order of Merit. In Tippett there is an unusual mixture of establishment and anti-establishment attitudes, of the traditionalist and the experimenter.

The fact that he has a fondness for pastel sneakers, television soap operas, and gently sending up his interviewers (who, along with everyone else he meets, he calls 'love') is partly the grand old man enjoying himself. But it is also demystification. Astron, in Tippett's fourth opera, *The Ice Break* (1973–76), might be the composer himself when he chides his sycophants: 'Saviour?! Hero?! Me?!! You must be joking!'

Tippett's visit to Australia was part of the latest in a series of overseas tours which began in the mid 1960s. This one was timed to

238

coincide with the composer's 85th birthday, although he neither looks nor behaves like any octogenarian I have ever met.

Apart from regular holidays in Europe, which he had taken since his youth, it was not until Tippett was invited to the 1965 Aspen Festival in Colorado that his feet became seriously itchy. His relationship with the United States has been variously described as a love affair and a new spiritual home, although Tippett himself (who was in something of a debunking mood on the day I met him) disagrees.

'The calls from America came because the music had gone over there, especially on tape. And once I was there, I was enormously moved by the place itself: the people, but also the different countryside, because I'd never seen it; I hadn't been to Australia then and I had never seen that kind of immense countryside. After that I got drawn into America in other ways. I began to read American history properly, found really what was what, and by a set of accidents went all over the place, to most of the major cities and down into Mexico and so forth, and I realised that it had opened up something in myself.

'From America I looked back at England and thought, "What a very beautiful island, but how tiny! And how concentrated!". So it changed me, but I would think that the people who say it was a new spiritual home for me are being very far-fetched, because—here we go!—I mean God knows what a "spiritual home" is. No, no, no. I followed the music there.'

Talking with Tippett about America prompted me to enquire how he found living in England these days. At the end of 1989 the Arts Council of Great Britain removed its funding grant to Kent Opera, of which Tippett was president. The Arts Council's decision which, in Tippett's words, was 'dictated by the government', prompted the composer to get involved, coming to Kent Opera's defence in an eloquent article in the *Guardian* newspaper. The decision remained, but Tippett's stand had an impact.

'It hasn't altered the government,' Tippett admits, 'but there'll be another one. I was always left-wing and not right-wing and as [Thatcher's government] became more and more divisive, and between rich and poor the divisions got stronger and stronger, it was unhappy government, it seemed to me, and an unhappy state. It'll be put back again.'

I wondered whether Tippett's optimism was misplaced; so much of Thatcher's socio-economic change seems irreparable.

'Oh, no! Oh no, I've seen it before, love. You see I go back so far. I remember what the problem was after the first world war. But imagine what is going to happen when another government comes and tries to repair the whole country—the health service, education, whatever. I don't see that the priorities will be art as such; I don't think they *can* be. But nevertheless I would think that the promises that have been made may reasonably be kept, because, what the hell, it's peanuts, the amount of money it's going to cost, and yet the whole musical profession needs it badly—and it's a huge industry.'

Tippett's musical career is marked out by five large-scale operatic utterances. Each of these dramatic works has been problematic to some extent. *The Midsummer Marriage* (1946–52), the first of them, is a score of great lyrical luminosity, although it did not always appear that way. The sprung rhythms and detailed orchestration seemed clumsy and opaque to many listeners at the first performances in 1955. The composer's second opera, *King Priam*, startled audiences for almost exactly opposite reasons. In dealing with the history of the Trojan Wars, Tippett evolved a far leaner and more direct musical style. *The Knot Garden* (1966–70) and *The Ice Break* belong to the 1960s and 1970s, spiritually as much as chronologically. These were accused of being trendy. Now, with his fifth opera, *New Year*, premiered in late 1989 in Houston, Texas, Tippett seems to be re-exploring his most lyrical uses of musical language, in a work that deals with contemporary life in a somewhat futuristic manner. There is even a female embodiment of evil amongst the dramatis personae who bears a striking resemblance to Margaret Thatcher.

What principally distinguishes Tippett's operas is the fact that he is his own librettist. And, truth to tell, it has been the librettos which have caught most of the criticism. They are frequently emblematic, they quote extensively (from Shakespeare, Yeats, Jung) and they marry high-flown, mystical poesy with banal street talk.

The composer has often sought advice from others on his text writing. T.S. Eliot, most notably, encouraged him in the first place to be his own librettist. But Tippett has also appreciated the need, with stage works, to consult directors. Before *King Priam*, the advice Tippett received was to put his intentions on a postcard to distil the dramatic nature of the work. Tippett now considers such advice invaluable.

What emerges from the operatic canon, now that the individual works have received performances that fully reveal their true nature, are their humanitarian concerns. On the one hand there is a concern with social issues, on the other is the Jungian requirement for both society and the individual person to acknowledge their essential dualities in order to learn and to grow. As the composer put it in 1941, in his first libretto, for his oratorio *A Child of Our Time*: 'I would know my shadow and my light,/so shall I at last be whole . . .'

Tippett's humanitarianism takes many forms, not least of which is his work with young composers. Although he has never formally taught composition (he taught modern languages for a time), his travelling over the last 25 years has brought him into contact with students from a wide range of cultures and backgrounds. As someone who knows the value of good advice, Tippett now ponders the difficulties facing young composers today and wonders whether it is possible to offer them much by way of helpful counsel.

'If we are moving—as we are, to some degree—towards one world, then what are going to be the possible metaphors, musical and otherwise, for such a diversity of planetary races? I don't think we know the answer. So that when a young composer is in college in the present day, he may find quite a difficulty in finding what he wants to be or how to do it.

'For that reason there have been the pulls of certain very obvious fashions, some of them very unrelated to localities, which have drawn composers. I have never had that problem because I am older and have stayed my own way, but moved all the time towards exploring the possibilities of making works of art which could move across the frontiers, or some frontiers.

'And then, as Verdi said, most composers would like to live in an ivory tower, but they have to live in the marketplace. I would accept that. So what does the marketplace imply? That is the difficulty.

'I don't belong to any school and I never have. I don't want that complexity that is impenetrable, that is absolutely clear. In my younger days there was a composer, I think he was Indian, called Sorabji, who lived in England and wrote the most complex pieces of piano music ever. Well, it hasn't succeeded, because it became beyond the pale of complexity.

'Minimalism, I think, has the danger of being dull. I can't put it any better than that.

'I can't give advice to a young composer. I think they have to find who they are themselves. We did too; I was no different. I had to find what my own song was and it took me till I was nearly 30 before I got there.'

I mentioned to Tippett that the first time I had met him, as a student composer myself, he had given me some very valuable advice. I had just completed a piece which was extremely complex and I was very proud of it, but then it was played and I had never heard anything so boring. For all my use of mathematical procedures, there was nothing of interest in the music. Tippett had said, 'Just use your ears, love.'

Thirteen years later Tippett found this story remarkably amusing ('Did I really say that?'), but at the time it was what I had needed to hear. As advice it may have been oversimple and rather extreme, but it altered my whole approach to composition and set me on the road to finding my own voice. There must be literally hundreds of composers around the world who can point to similar encounters with Tippett and who feel, as I do, that the meeting marked a watershed in their development.

As I headed down Albert Street, turning over in my mind this latest conversation with the composer, I could not help wishing I had taken up his offer of a swap. It seemed just the sort of day for padding through the streets of Brisbane in my socks, wearing Sir Michael Tippett's mortar-board.

Brisbane, March 1990

Glossary of musical terms

aleatoricism   Strictly speaking, the elements of aleatoric music are determined by chance (the throw of dice or I Ching). Through misuse, however, the term 'aleatoric' is often applied today to any music which contains indeterminate passages, even though these may have been strictly notated by the composer and involve no chance procedures at all. A work such as Boulez's Piano Sonata No.3, for example, in which the performer determines the order of the music according to rules set down by the composer, is more accurately termed a 'mobile score'.

atonal   The absence of **tonality**. Since the experience of tonality or tonal relationships is essentially in the ear of the beholder, 'atonality' is a term more popular than precise. Some would argue that genuinely atonal music is an impossibility. See **non-tonal**.

automatism   Composing with a numerical formula or algorithm which dictates some or all aspects of a piece.

buffa   Italian for 'comic'. Hence opera buffa: 'comic opera'.

cantata   A work for voice (or voices) and instruments, generally to a secular text (as opposed to an oratorio which is usually biblical).

cantus firmus   A melodic line—most often plainsong—which repeats throughout a piece and to which the other parts may or may not be related. In medieval and Renaissance music the cantus firmus is generally sung or played in long, slow notes, surrounded by other more elaborate parts.

chromaticism   The use of scales consisting of semitones. Chromatic harmony is the opposite of **diatonic**; it stretches **tonality**. Extreme chromaticism avoids tonality.

claves   A percussion instrument prevalent in Latin-American music, but having its origins in Africa. It consists of two cylindrical, wooden sticks; one clave is rested on the cupped palm of a hand (which acts as a resonator) and struck with the other clave.

continuo   In baroque music this is the function of supporting and filling out the music, generally undertaken by a harpsichord and cello. Other instruments such as an organ or a lute can also fulfil this function.

diatonic   Equal-tempered major and minor scales. In common usage, diatonic harmony is the simplest form of **tonality**.

dodecaphony   See **serialism**.

242

expressionism   A term from the visual arts. It refers to the early 20th century movement in Austria and Germany which took dreams, nightmares and the workings of the subconscious as its subject matter, often with a deliberately overblown style. Schoenberg's *Pierrot lunaire* and *Erwartung* are good examples of musical expressionism.

gamelan   The percussion orchestra of Bali and Java.

impressionism   A term taken from the visual arts. It is often (misleadingly?) applied to music with descriptive titles by French composers such as Debussy and Ravel. Today any music which employs harmonies, textures and instrumental effects reminiscent of those composers is liable to be dubbed 'impressionistic'.

maximalism   Response to the term **minimalism**. Music which employs an especially large amount of material. Maximalist scores tend to be dense with information. The music is generally highly chromatic. Its critics say it is complex to the point of impenetrability; its exponents prefer descriptions such as 'rich'.

minimalism   From the visual arts and first applied to music by Michael Nyman. This is music which employs a tiny amount of material, often slowly transforming it over a long time span. It tends to be rhythmically repetitious and harmonically limited. Its critics call it boring; its exponents prefer terms such as 'hypnotic'.

mode   Tones organised into a scale; strictly speaking, any scale is a mode. In practice, however, 'modal' is a term used to refer to music which is neither organised in terms of major and minor keys, nor '**atonal**', but which nevertheless employs scales (such as the Greek or church modes, whole-tone or **pentatonic** scales).

modernism   These days this is a very loaded term. It has come to imply works of art, particularly from the first half of the 20th century, which were experimental in nature and sought to advance the language of their medium and genre. Musical modernists would include Schoenberg, Berg, Webern, Stravinsky, Varèse and Boulez. Although apparently radical in intent, the modernist outlook is today considered 'conservative' and outmoded by post-modernists who dispute the notion of progress as historically inevitable or even desirable.

neo-classicism   In a sense this is an early version of post-modernism (see **modernism**). In the 20th century (and there were, arguably, musical neo-classicists in previous centuries) the term is usually associated with Stravinsky's music from the mid 1920s until the early 1950s. He and his followers appropriated formal models and musical gestures from Bach to Mozart in an attempt to make music more 'objective'. Neo-classical works tend to be uncluttered, rather transparently scored and frequently employ chugging motor rhythms of the sort found in Bach's *Brandenburg* concertos.

neo-romanticism   A more recent development than **neo-classicism** and a more explicit rejection of **modernism**, particularly of **non-tonal** harmonies, fragmented melodic lines and disjunct rhythms. Neo-romantic music tends to be tonal and lushly (sometimes garishly) scored.

non-tonal   The avoidance of **tonality**. This is a rather more accurate term than '**atonal**' for describing music of extreme **chromaticism**. Schoenberg's pieces composed immediately before World War I are non-tonal in that they strive never to be in a key. However, to call them 'atonal' implies that they are devoid of tonal centres, which is demonstrably untrue.

note row   See **serialism**.

organum   A simple form of part-singing, usually in parallel fourths and fifths, associated with the medieval church.

ostinato   A continuously repeated rhythmic or melodic pattern.

pentatonic   A simple five-note scale, derived directly from the harmonic series. It is the basis of most of the world's folk music. You can easily locate a pentatonic scale by playing only on the black notes of a keyboard.

rebec   A small, pear-shaped medieval fiddle of thin but penetrating tone.

reverb   Reverberation. The way a note 'hangs in the air' after the attack. Unlike an echo—where the attack is heard again (and again)—reverberation consists of echoes in an enclosed space, so numerous as to be indistinguishable from each other. Acoustics are more or less reverberative. Reverb can also be added electronically to a tone or noise.

sackbut   A brass instrument with a slide, common in the Renaissance. The precursor of the modern trombone.

sampler   To sample a sound is to make a digital recording of it, such that it can be played back in a variety of ways. For example, a voice might be sampled and then played back on a keyboard at different pitches.

serialism   Also known as **dodecaphony**. The organisation of the twelve chromatic tones into a sequence of 'row', from whose order all the pitch material (melodic and harmonic) of a piece is derived. A 'row' or 'series' may be transposed or used in inversion (upside-down) or retrograde (backwards), but the internal relationships of intervals will always remain. In strict serialism, the order in which these intervals appear will be maintained. To this extent, it resembles the medieval **cantus firmus**. However, the series is not a theme; it can rarely be perceived with the ear, and sometimes only located after prolonged analysis of a score. Serialism was developed by the second Viennese school (Schoenberg, Berg and Webern) to impose order on non-tonal music. Later composers, such as Boulez, Stockhausen, Barraqué and Babbitt, took serialism further in the 1950s, using the series to dictate not only pitch but also the lengths of notes (and rests), their dynamics, timbres and so forth. This became known as '**integral serialism**'.

shawm   A reed instrument of Middle Eastern origin, common in Europe after the Crusades and still found today in Arab countries. The precursor of the modern oboe.

tam-tam   A large, flat, untuned gong.

tonality   In common usage this refers to music which employs the system of Western tempered major and minor keys and the relationships between them. So-called 'tonal' music invariably has a home key or 'tonic' to which all other keys have a more or less close relationship. In chromatic tonal music (Wagner, Bruckner, Mahler) the more distant relationships tend to be explored.

tone row   See **serialism**.

twelve-tone music   See **serialism**.

Index